THE RESILIENT FARMER

THE RESILIENT FARMER

Weathering the challenges of life and the land

DOUG AVERY
WITH MARGIE THOMSON

Contents

PART FOUR

I dedicate this book to my wife Wendy and
to my amazing extended family

FOREWORD

Up until about five years ago, probably like every other non-rural New Zealander, I thought most farmers had an idyllic life. They live in beautiful places, away from the stresses of the concrete jungle. They commune with nature on a daily basis. And they're all rich, aren't they?

But then I saw the 2012 report commissioned by Farmsafe in response to some earlier findings by the coroner, revealing high levels of suicide among our farmers. At that stage, the number was on average twenty-five suicides per year. In addition to suicide, there are suicide attempts that, although they might not result in death, cause distress and concern to individuals and their families.

Each one of those suicides and attempted suicides are, as Doug shows in this book, the tip of an iceberg made of distress, depression and busted lives and relationships.

When I saw that report, I was gobsmacked. I couldn't believe it. I thought, *We've got to do something about this.*

In the years since we'd established the www.depression.org website, we'd had great success reaching out to people. But I now understood we needed voices from the farming community, people able to relate to other country people better than I could. After all, what the hell would a city boy like me know about country pressures?

Fortunately, we became aware of a Marlborough farmer, Doug

Avery, who'd begun sharing his story about dealing with the pressures of drought, and his own journey out of depression. We heard he was keen to help out.

I flew down to Blenheim with a film crew and we drove the forty kilometres to Doug's house, staring out the windows of the car at the beautiful countryside. *Wow, this is a postcard!* City people always think that: *I'll come here for a holiday.*

Doug showed us around his farm and told me his story. Doug's an emotional man. He wears his heart on his sleeve, and he tears up pretty easily when he's talking about his tough times – not something you often see in any man, particularly a weather-beaten farmer. But I've rarely met a stronger person. It was hard to imagine he was once thinking about suicide and completely messed up like I'd been, because here in front of me was this guy who was full on – full of energy, wanting to change the world, and reaching out to help his fellow farmers.

We got the full treatment on the farm that day – Doug's wife Wendy cooked us an awesome lunch, we drove around Bonavaree, threw a ball about on the front lawn with Doug's grandkids and some of the farm guys. And I learned. I learned that my stereotype was just that – it had blinded me to the realities of modern farming.

I learned that amid the beauty of the landscape was sheer challenge. The hills were dry. It wasn't hard to see the contrast between those barren hills and the brilliant green of Doug's lucerne. I realised what Doug was up against, not just in his own landscape, but in the world – giant global economies control commodity prices and God controls the weather! These are two of the biggest stressors in a farmer's life, and they have no control over either.

'I don't know how you do it,' I said to Doug.

What Doug had found inside himself was a true resilience, an attitude and approach to life that we all – rural or urban – needed to hear about.

If you look at a rugby team, you can see that certain personalities congregate in certain positions, right? Wingers are show ponies; props are quiet achievers – it's the same all over the world. And it's not just with rugby, it's the same in any job, to an extent. If you look at our farmers, traditionally, they tend to be introverts – they have to be, to handle the isolation. They are strong people. Stoic. Their self-belief centres on being able to cope with everything the land throws at them. So mental health, for them, is pretty complex. The idea of showing vulnerability is probably several times more traumatic than it is for someone like me. They look to their family background – maybe they're the third or fourth generation on that piece of land – and they think, *My parents and grandparents built this farm, cleared it with their own hands; am I going to lose it?* They think, *My parents and grandparents never got depressed; what's wrong with me?* They don't realise that, often, their parents and grandparents actually did suffer, but they hid it. That's certainly the case with Doug.

The reaction of many farmers to feeling bad is to work harder, isolate themselves more – both of which only make things worse.

These are very strong people. And an important message bears repeating: depression is not a weakness; it's an illness.

When Doug's video went up on www.depression.org, there were something like 18,000 hits and 3800 people specifically watched Doug telling his story. So I know he made a difference right away.

Years ago, when we did the initial advertising campaign for the Ministry of Health, where I went on TV and talked about my experiences with depression, the big impact on New Zealanders was: *If it's okay for an All Black to admit he's depressed, then it's okay for me.* That was a powerful message, and people still tell me that today.

What Doug's done is take it a step further. Here's a farmer, talking openly about the stress his job puts him under. He's put it into terms that other rural people can understand, and that saves lives. Doug Avery literally saves lives.

I'm a city boy; Doug's a country boy. Our lives have been very different – yet we both got tackled and brought down by the horrible illness of depression. We both learned how to manage that illness and to get on our journey to wellness.

An image sticks in my mind. A woman, who came up to talk to me after a presentation I'd made to a large group of rural people in a North Island town. She was young – had a babe in her arms and two other young kids hanging on to her legs. Just weeks before, her husband, a farmer, had killed himself in their cowshed. This woman has stayed with me for the rawness of her loss, but sadly she's one of many I've met who have lost a loved one to despair. More than I can count.

That's why Doug is so important. He has much to offer in this book. Read it, give it to a friend. We need to keep talking about this, and sharing our stories. I believe that's how we'll change things.

Sir John Kirwan

PROLOGUE

The engine noise breaks across the paddock and the sheep lift their heads. They surge together, dirty white against the scorched hills, and stream towards me, pushing to get the hay I chuck off the back of the truck. They think I'm their best friend. Their cries scrape the hot air, their hooves churn the dry earth and dust rises in great clouds all around. My own boots make no mark on the ground, and my eyes and mouth fill with grit. My heart is sick.

My animals will not go hungry, but I am failing. A drought is a slow death, and this one has already gone on three years and thank God I don't know it will go for a further five. Every day I watch my farm burn. Marlborough's hills bleached straw-yellow then became ash, so bare the earth's bones poke through, dusty and crumbling. Day after day, the sky is a relentless, empty blue. As our land dries up, all my hopes have also turned to vapour, lost in that wide, blue yonder.

I am so angry – but who do you be angry with, in a drought? When I get home that day, I drink, just like all the other days, and the beer goes down fast, followed by whatever, and I find I can be angry with everyone.

And then a moment of hope. Ridiculous hope – hope that feels like a desperate bargain, that everything will be alright and the land will burst forth with green again, and I will no longer have to toss feed to my animals. Clouds, grey and fat with the promise of rain, saunter over the north-west horizon and hang there in the distance, shadows against the blue.

I find myself outside my house, my feet on the lawn, amid the tiny oasis my wife has created to make me feel better. A garden of green and bright colours amid the grey hills. But it doesn't make me feel better; nothing does. I am filled with rage. So *much* rage. I raise my fists to that impassive sky and I bellow like a bull. And those clouds, those beautiful, dark, moisture-filled clouds, vanish out to sea. And my wife, who has also felt the lash of my anger and my nasty, drunken misery, watches me through the windows of our front room, and is afraid and helpless.

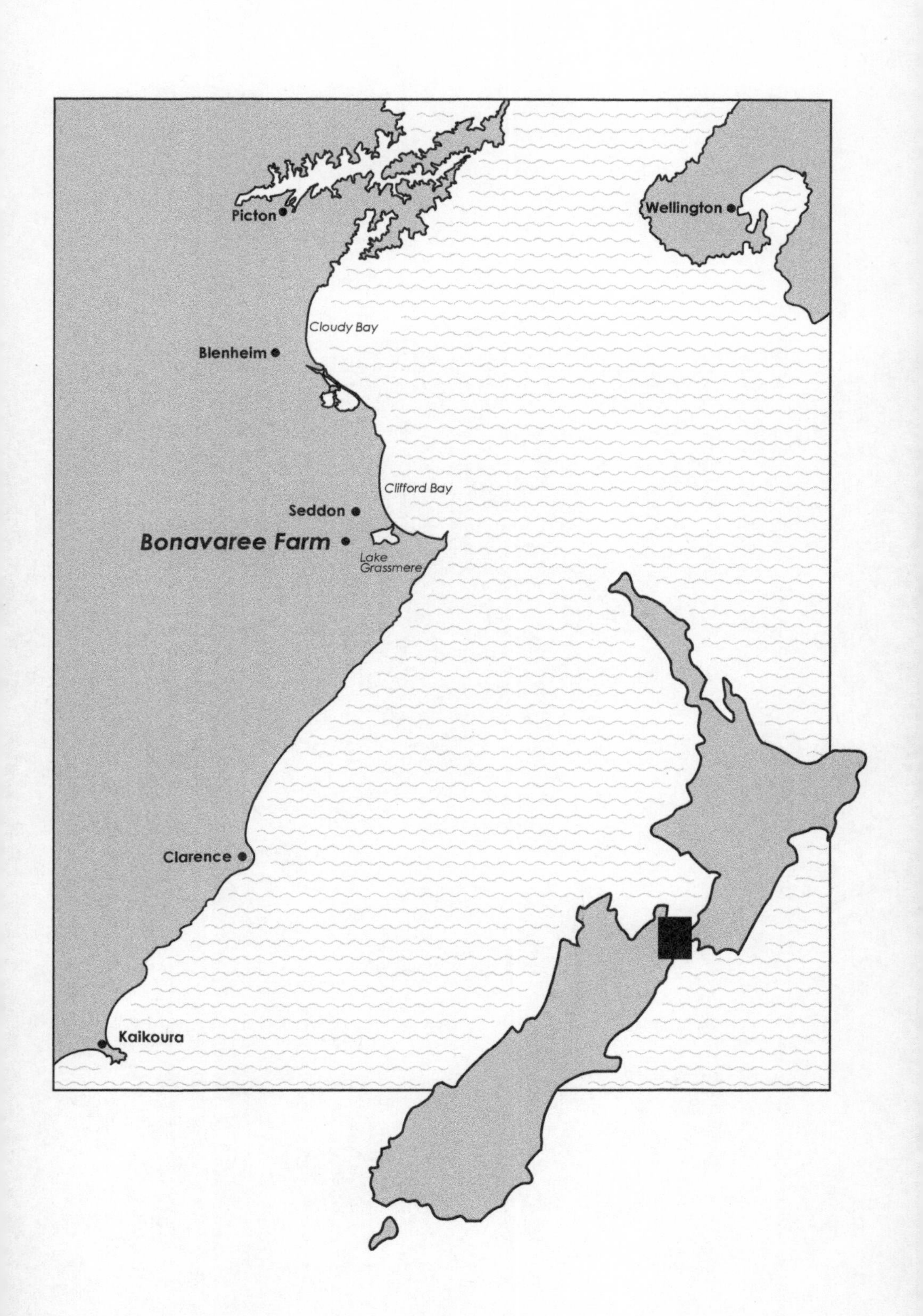
Picton
Wellington
Cloudy Bay
Blenheim
Clifford Bay
Seddon
Bonavaree Farm
Lake Grassmere
Clarence
Kaikoura

PART ONE

1

MY TOP PADDOCK

Eight years, the drought lasted. Then no sooner had we learned how to deal with that than nature sent us a wind that roared in like a high-speed train at 225 kilometres an hour, demolishing our fence lines and trees, our stoic stands of radiata pines, eucalypts and macrocarpas, as if they were skittles.

Even then she hadn't done with us. Just weeks after the wind, in 2013, we were smashed by a magnitude 6.6 earthquake whose epicentre was only a couple of kilometres down the road. Our possessions were broken, and sooty bricks ricocheted through the rooms of our beloved home. In November 2016 we had a second earthquake that made the first seem like a pup – 7.8 magnitude. It terrorised our small rural community and deranged the land itself, lifting our entire farm, fortunately in one section, two metres higher and five metres north, brought hillsides crashing down, and tossed us all around as if we were nothing.

If we hadn't realised it before, surely we know it now: we humans are like fleas on an elephant, just a minuscule part of the great, rolling processes of our planet. Droughts, wind, earthquakes . . . we can't stop these things happening. Nor can we escape the usual ups and downs of life: our family, like yours, has had its trials, its cancer scares, its timely and untimely deaths. Governments make good and bad policies that help or hurt us; the global economy is a force that must always be reckoned with. For farming folk as for everybody else, the really big things in life are outside our control. The only thing we *can* control is how we meet these challenges.

The first five of those drought years, things got pretty ugly for me, and I dived into a very dark pit. No matter what I did, I was unsuccessful. I had a destroyed farm, a destroyed bank account and destroyed hopes. The feeling of failure struck at the very core of my being: I thrive on reward, and that had vanished from my life. I was so ashamed and afraid, and yet so determined to blame everyone – anything – else for my problems. I was that man who wouldn't come to the phone, who pushed everyone away, who bristled with anger and impatience, and who drank himself to sleep every night. I was that man who did his best to make his own wife leave him so there'd be no one left to witness the shame. I came pretty close to being the man who gets to the end of his tether and just ends it all.

All that saved me was a bit of luck. Help came to find me, in the form of a young sales rep who was pushy enough to make me leave the farm for a day. I didn't want to go, couldn't see the use, but he turned up anyway and made me get in his car and go with him to a field day down in Waipara. And on that day I got handed some hope: hope in the form of a new idea, a solution to a problem I hadn't yet understood. I thought my problem was drought; it wasn't. My problem was the way I farmed, and the way I thought about things.

Even at my lowest point, I wanted to find a solution. I remember sitting with a neighbouring farmer, my friend Kev Loe, looking out at the hillsides, the way they were splitting open under the sun's blowtorch, knowing we had no water for our animals, feeling disgusted and ashamed and gutted. He said to me: 'There's as much opportunity out there, Doug, as there's ever been – it's just, have we got the eyes to see it?' I thought and thought about that. I wrote it down on a piece of paper and put it beside my computer. I used to stare at that bit of paper and think: 'But what . . .? And how? *How?*'

Well, he was right about the opportunity, but I was never going to find the answer on my own. I wasn't even asking the right question. 'How?' was not the place to start. I was still some years away from meeting the guy who would teach me the real question to ask.

Way back then, the new idea that rescued me and set me off on my process of discovery and change came in the form of a plant – a plant we'd been growing for eighty years, but hadn't seen the potential of: lucerne, whose long tap root has the power to transform the way we utilise water. I've since been dubbed 'the Lucerne Lunatic' for my endless attempts to spread the word to other farmers. But, as a friend of mine said: 'Doug, your story's not really about lucerne, is it?'

'No,' I agreed. 'It just happened to be our tool. This is a story about changing the way we integrate into the world.'

That new idea eventually led to me farm differently and over the years took me from failure to success, with a ton of help along the way. I went from zero income in 1998 to winning South Island Farmer of the Year in 2010. We've increased our land holdings and massively increased our outputs and our profitability, while being far more environmentally friendly. We are the same family with the same farms in the same valley in the same climate. The world hasn't changed, but the story has changed. We turned our system on its head and we became a success story.

Learning to farm differently – to farm with nature, rather than against it – is at the heart of that success. But, even more important, I had to change my thinking processes. I became emotionally resilient. Now, I always put that first. I have no comprehension how people can run businesses of any kind if they're not emotionally strong.

In the last few years, my interest in life has turned to the management of my own head. My top paddock. Any of us, rural or urban, can do well, but only if we untangle the processes of our own minds.

I'm not a book-learned person. I learn from life, from my experiences, and most of all from those around me, and I've been lucky to meet some wonderful people. They probably all thought I was talking too much to take in anything they were saying, but I was listening. Sponge-learning – that's what I do. My great motivating desire is not to be better than anyone else but to be better than I used to be. Self-improvement is at the core of this man.

My story is not just about agriculture. It's about having life go badly wrong, but finding solutions that work. It's about learning to pick the people who can help you create solutions, as opposed to those who can just further the damage.

We have been helped to find incredible success here at Bonavaree, and now my journey is around sharing the things that made a difference to me. Good people don't stop and run off with the prize. They try to create and enhance the opportunity for a prize for somebody else.

2

MY PLACE IN THE WORLD

Farming was all I ever wanted to do. The farm is my happy place. It has always been so, since my earliest days, apart from those few years when it seemed to turn against me.

Our family has farmed at Bonavaree, in the south-east of the Marlborough district in the South Island, since 1919. It's one of the oldest sheep-farming areas in the South Island, and the driest part of the country, lying in the rain shadow of the Kaikoura Ranges.

I live in the house my grandparents, Ern and Amy Avery, lived in when they first came to the farm, and in which first my father, then I and my siblings, and then my own children, grew up. My mother, Joyce, grew up just outside of Ward, about ten kilometres south of here. Our roots are deep.

Believe it or not, the farm's name has nothing to do with the fact that Averys farm here. It was already called Bonavaree when my grandparents bought it, named by the first people who farmed there.

But the truck drivers have always written *Bon Avery*.

In those days it was 206 hectares – it's grown tenfold since I began farming – and they ran Corriedales and cattle. It's always been parched land, but they farmed as they knew how and managed to turn enough profit to make it worthwhile. My father was a dynamo; he'd go all day and he achieved very successfully at his level – the small family farm. From him I learnt that hard work was the thing you did to become successful.

Much of Marlborough is now given over to the wine industry, which thrives on the Mediterranean character of the weather here: the hot summers and mild winters, and the famous dryness. But for traditional farming, it's challenging. To give you an idea: our nearest neighbour is the Lake Grassmere salt works. There, the long, dry summers and the warm north-west winds are ideal. Water evaporates quickly off the holding ponds, leaving behind crusts of salt, to be harvested into huge mounds of glittering white salt.

These sparkling piles are easily seen from State Highway 1, which rushes past, south to Kaikoura and Christchurch, and north to Blenheim and Picton. In our toughest year, when I was a dried-out husk of a man and our farm was on the brink of disaster, the salt works turned its biggest profit ever. At the peak of that summer they pumped more water each day from the sea into the lake than Auckland City uses, and the level of the lake still went down with evaporation. They are an icon to the nature of this place, a constant reminder of the harsh, thirsty climate.

Those same nor'westerlies beloved by the salt works are brutal for us. During the drought, in the early summer of 1997, we had ninety days when it never stopped blowing. It howled day and night, unceasing, and broke us all. Now and again it would stop for a few minutes and blow from the south, and then it would go back to the north-west. I don't think anything has demoralised me more. We watched the manure gusting around the paddocks, piling up against the fences – dried out like little marbles, almost as light as air.

Lying almost adjacent to us across the Southern Alps, on the West Coast of the South Island, the city of Westport gets average rainfall of about 2000 millimetres a year. Across Cook Strait, Wellington, whose hills and coastline are visible from high parts of our farm, gets an average of about 1250 millimetres a year. Most areas of New Zealand have between 600 and 1600 millimetres.

The average in our area, taken over the last 100 years, is 570 millimetres. And for seventeen out of nineteen years, between 1988 and 2007, the farm got below-average rainfall. Through the 1990s and into the 2000s we experienced the driest years on record, with eight of them, from 1997 on, being drought years. The least rainfall we've ever had was in 1997 and that was just 315 millimetres. The creek I played in as a child was bone-dry for thirteen years.

It's a ridiculous place to farm.

But this is where we're from, and the dryness also gives us so much beauty: the tawny colours, the crisp light, the razor-edged shadows that reveal the rolling contours of our hills, and the endless blue sky that gleams above us. Our blood, sweat and tears are on this land. Generation after generation, we've fallen in love with it. My wife, Wendy, is from here, too – her family farmed just fourteen kilometres south-east of here; from up on the hills behind our farmhouse, we can easily see the trees around her childhood home.

In 2002 our son Fraser came home and he's since taken over the running of the farm, and now it's his kids who are running around, learning the rhythms of this place, as connected to nature as it's possible to be.

What I remember, what I know about myself that's been true all my life, is this amazing feeling for the delights of the seasons. I've always loved the seasonality of agriculture, and the way the seasons work here when they're unfolding in the order that makes us happy. The joy of summer's heat and dry; autumn's quick flush and beautiful rain; the frosty winters when we draw breath and prepare for the next unfolding; and then spring, bursting upon us with its brilliant green, so fresh and lush it could break my heart with happiness.

We take joy in eating all the seasonal foods that we grow or buy. Spring, when we tuck into new-season asparagus with bacon. Summer, when the beautiful plum tree right by our house is laden with fruit. (As a child it was a punishment to pick up the thousands of windfall plums.) Our vege gardening has always focused on summer production: new potatoes, with home-grown mint. Peas, baby carrots and beans; strawberries and raspberries. The pleasure, just before Christmas, of going to the cherry orchards and picking my own. Oh, I have had some upset tummies. That is the owner's revenge.

Late-summer peaches. Autumn, and we pour bowls of creamy mushroom soup. Winter, we're comforted by glorious pumpkin soup with heaps of garlic, and beaut roast dinners. We love our lamb and beef. Most farmers like older sheep, but at Bonavaree we dine on our very best lamb and our best beef. We love this all year.

All these delights, all to do with the natural flow and contrast of the seasons. These are special times throughout the year that I look forward to so much. When the first lambs and the first calves are born here every year, it's just so exciting. I still feel that today.

But when you can't provide for them in the way that you feel you should, that you know you should, the feeling is completely opposite.

3

PEAKS AND VALLEYS

When I was young I wanted to climb One Tree Hill, the hill that stands to our south at the end of Grassmere Valley. My mother said it was too hard and too high and too far and too dangerous. But when I was about nine, I got a group of friends together one day and we began to climb. When I got near the top I realised Mum was right. It was further than I had thought, and it was hard work, but I was determined to prove that she was wrong.

Soon we were standing on the top looking over the tawny grasslands of Grassmere and out to the big, wide ocean, and I was so proud of my achievement. I couldn't believe what we'd done. But now I could see I wasn't on the top at all. Behind us now, even further south, was a huge mountain that loomed over the horizon, seeming to dwarf everything. I was looking at Tapuaenuku, the highest New Zealand peak outside the Southern Alps. Edmund Hillary himself scaled it solo over a weekend in 1944 and said he'd 'climbed a decent mountain at last'. I thought, *Far out, I've climbed nothing.*

That's what life's like. That is actually what it's like.

I've since climbed Tapuaenuku – Tappy, we locals call it – seven times, the first when I was fifteen. It's my peak. Up there, the view sweeps from the Port Hills of Christchurch to Motueka, and across to the lower North Island. Every time I've stood on the summit the view has taken my breath away.

But here's a life truth: no one can stay on the summit. We can't live our life up there; there is nothing to sustain people on peaks. Everyone must return again to the valleys and the flats where most of our lives are lived. This is as true of life as it is of mountaineering.

Beyond every peak that I've climbed is another great challenge. Between every peak there is a valley, and valleys are just as vital as peaks. They are places where you can rest and relax and start generating the energy and mental capacity to climb your next peak.

Life's a journey of peaks and valleys. We all dream of being on the peak – we dream of glory, of achievement, the respect or admiration of our peers – but most of our lives are spent in valleys. Peaks and valleys, I think, is a lovely concept for people. If you are mindful of peaks and valleys, you never become mired in despair.

I was the youngest child of four. I have a sister, Alison, eight years older, a brother Basil six years older, and another brother, Eric, who was two-and-a-half years older than me and with whom I was always in conflict, him fighting me, me fighting him. The two older ones went off to boarding school around the time I began primary school so, although they were heroes to me, I didn't know them well in my childhood.

It was my father I most revered and loved to be with, and being with him, working with him on the farm, is at the heart of my childhood memories. I feel as though he indoctrinated me into this environment and this life.

Dad – Graham Avery – was a hero even before I came into the world. He'd been a Royal Air Force navigator of a Lancaster bomber in World War II, and received the Distinguished Flying Cross for services way in excess of what was required. But to me, before I knew anything about his war experiences, he was a hero because of the way that he farmed, and for his values of service and contribution.

His favourite saying was: 'We're each given two hands: one to help ourselves and one to help others.' And that's how he lived. He could feed and maintain his family with half his work all his life, and then the other half he could give to the greater good – county council, school committees, church, Lions Club and much more. My father didn't understand people who didn't have a service mentality. If everyone was like him, we would be living in a world of abundance.

He had seen what greed could do to the world. He described it to me as the greatest sin. Flying over Germany, he came to the conclusion that greed lay behind the destructiveness of war. He had no conscience about fighting the Nazis, believing it to have been a necessary war – although he would have been a conscientious objector in the Vietnam War – but the experience of bombing civilians stayed with him and shaped him for the rest of his life.

He said the squadrons were never told they were bombing civilian targets, but the men in the planes could tell. When they hit a factory the whole sky would light up. When they hit houses it was just *put, put, put, put*, and he said mostly they were just hitting women and children and houses and when they got back to England that's exactly what was happening there, so what do you do?

War showed him that it's not money that drives human achievement. My father always said to me, 'Before the war, Doug, the world economy was completely ruined, but the day after war broke

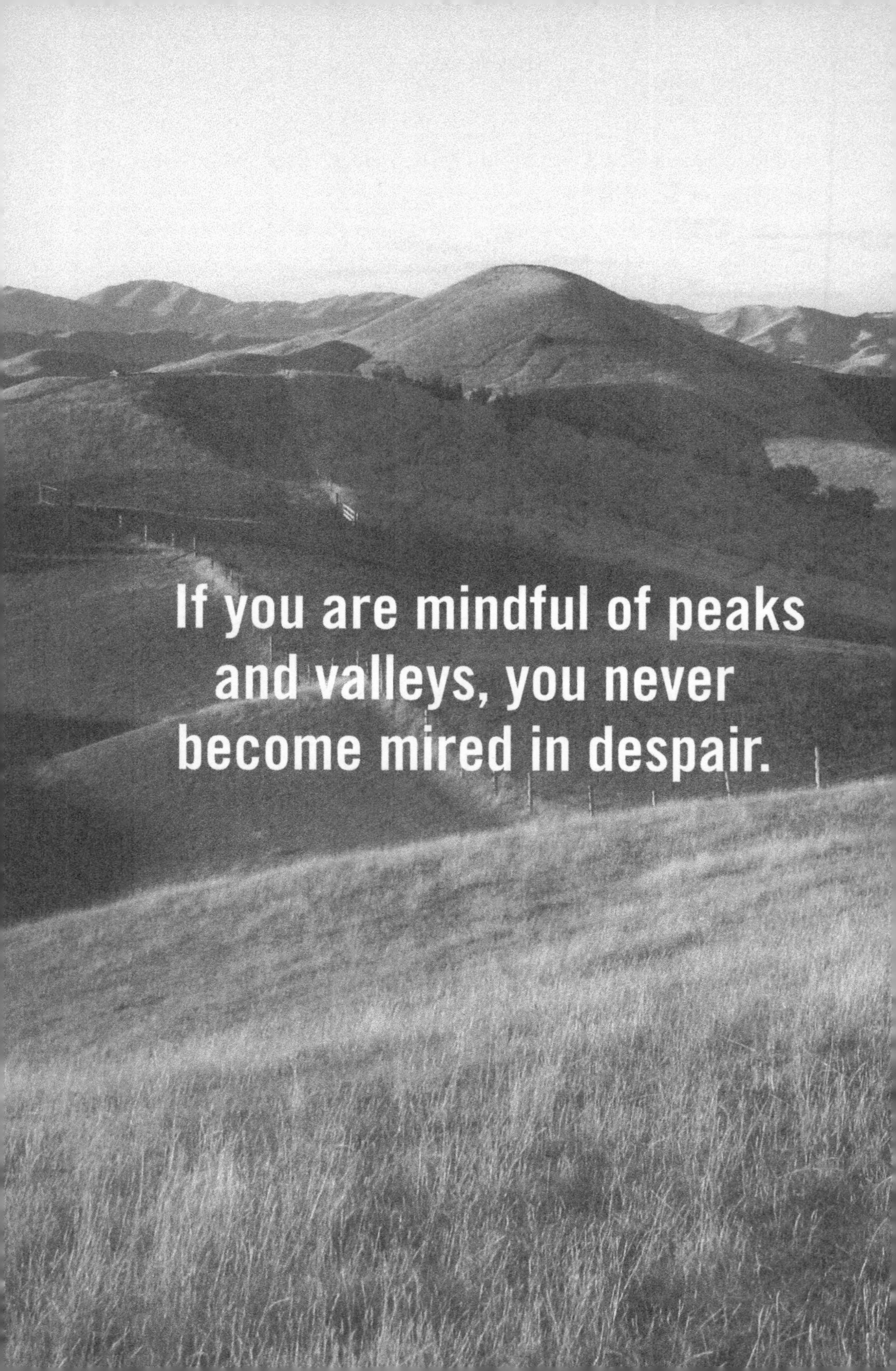

If you are mindful of peaks and valleys, you never become mired in despair.

out no one ever talked of money again. The only limitation of man then was what man could achieve.' Then he added: 'Isn't that true every day?' I said, 'You're right.'

He voted Social Credit in the years when that party was a presence in New Zealand politics, and people used to tease me – 'Your father's a funny money man,' they said – but he believed progress should be led by the human need for self-development, and that the system should serve this need, rather than the prevailing system where people serve the financial system.

Dad wasn't a mainstream thinker, and he indoctrinated me to not be afraid to think differently. Perhaps he made it natural for me to shift outside conventional thinking.

An example from his farming years was when the fertiliser companies – which were fast growing in influence – convinced most farmers to spray their lucerne against bugs and pests. Dad didn't like that idea, and instead he encouraged the birds into the lucerne crops by trailing wheat around the paddocks and into the crop to attract them, and planted trees for them to settle in. These days, that would be called organic; to him, it was just common sense.

But as a young child, all these big ideas were just the invisible texture of life. In those days it was the visible, visceral details of life that bewitched and delighted me, that captured me just as certainly as we used to tether lost lambs to mothered lambs, so that they, too, would learn to feed.

We lived very much off the land, as Wendy and I do today. It's the milk that I have special memories of. Dad would take a three-legged stool out into the paddock to the cow. 'Wooo,' he'd say. 'Wooo, girl,' and the cow would stand while he sat on the stool, placing a gleaming stainless steel bucket between his knees. Then, *squoosh, squoosh*, his hands compressed her teats and the milk gradually filled the bucket. He spoke gently to her as he worked, and she took the time to relax and chew her cud, occasionally belching up a bit of grass gas, a hot and unpleasant smell. When the bucket was full, we'd take it together to an outbuilding at the back of our house where we had a separator. I loved to crank up the separator. With every turn of the handle a bell would ding, and when I got it fast enough Dad would turn the tap and the still-warm milk would flow through the machine, cream out one spout and skimmed milk out the other.

Besides the eager calves that drank the skim milk I would usually take a cupful for myself, drinking it warm. It was always a special thing to do. Mum would make butter from the cream and cheese from the milk.

In that environment, we all contributed. I was always part of a team – our family team, contributing to our life together on the farm. As young people we did chores, which included feeding chooks and, as we grew older, milking the cows. I loved doing it, as I always wanted to be a part of what was going on.

I had a deal with Dad – I was always doing deals with him – from a town supply dairy farmer in Blenheim we used to get the top dairy heifer calves as they were born, and we reared them. We kept them for several years, put them in calf to a bull, and then they returned to the dairy farm to calve. When the calves were born we would buy those calves back to rear them, and so on. As my return on this investment, I was able to grow one or two of them and sell them as beef once they were fully matured. It was quite a long investment before you got a return, but it was a very good learning process. I later realised the teachings that my father did around learning to invest so that the rewards came in huge dividends.

The things I didn't enjoy: I went to Seddon Primary School, a bus ride away, which felt like I was rotting in hell, with teachers that were at best average, and at worst shocking. It wasn't a good start to academic life and left me in catch-up mode once I went to secondary school.

Mum and Dad were very religious. Church was a big part of their belief system, and also support system, especially for my mother, who in her early years of marriage had suffered from the isolation of our farm lifestyle. Dad was a Sunday school teacher, so we had to go, but I was always a reluctant participant.

I was also reluctant about my piano lessons. These took place in Ward, where I would see Wendy Loe; I would have been horrified at the time to think I was going to marry her. She had the lesson before me and used to wind the teacher up something shocking because she, too, was a reluctant student. By the time I arrived the music teacher was in bad fetter. I wasn't at all interested in girls. Mum used to say to me, 'Say hullo to the little girl Loe,' and I'd say, 'No.' Then it was time for my lesson and the moody teacher would whack me over the knuckles with a ruler because I hadn't done my scales.

On my eighth birthday I played my first game of organised rugby, and that was the best thing that ever happened to me in my life. For that first game I was placed in the backs, but next game the coach moved me to prop – he reckoned I needed to be in the thick of it. From then on, I played rugby continuously until I was about twenty-three or twenty-four – it was No. 1 right through my school years. Sunday, Monday and Tuesday was all talk about the last game, and from then on it was all focus on the next game.

Every year I played I got into the rep side, and as I got older I moved further out in the team, finishing as a winger. I just loved the teamwork and the physical side, but in my early twenties I started taking injuries – mostly torn cartilage – and it was buggering up my farming. So I gave the rugby away.

But as my boyhood years progressed, I continued to love being with Dad on the farm. In those days we didn't have utes, motorbikes and four-wheelers like we do now. We did a lot of the work off the tractor with a transport tray on the back. Lambing time was everybody to the tiller, as we used to close-lamb everything – help the ewes give birth, ensure the lambs learned to attach to their mother's teats – supervising every step of the way, and intervening when there were lamb deaths, which was a huge amount of work and very different to what's required today with our new breeds. Dad used to pick sheep up and shift them to better feed. I can't remember when I first began driving the tractor, but by the time I was eleven, I'd been driving for years. There was no such thing as Occupational Safety and Health in those days.

During haymaking, I drove the tractor while the men threw the hay onto the trailer. We had four David Brown tractors, and one was a crawler tractor, a little tracked vehicle onto which Dad used to hook lots of stuff, and I'd spend all day and all night out there working, loving it.

Life was good. And then everything changed.

The twenty-first of May, 1966. How can one family's life change in just one day? I was eleven, it was the school holidays, and my oldest brother Bas asked me if I wanted to go watch the senior rugby players play their Saturday game in Seddon. My next-oldest brother Eric didn't want to come – he was keen to go out hunting. So Bas and I went off, and by the time we got home, Eric was still out. As darkness fell, he still hadn't come in, and people began arriving to look for him. By six o'clock the next morning just about the whole district was out. The police coordinated the search, and they said if any of the teams found him, they were to come back to the farmhouse and three shots of the gun would be fired in the air.

I was out with one of the search parties, just half a kilometre or so from the house, when the three shots echoed over the land and I thought, *Oh, good, he's all right.*

But he wasn't all right. Bas was in the team that found him, and he's described seeing Eric there, lying face down, the wound in his head out of sight. Bas was the only member of our family that ever saw Eric's body. The doctor firmly advised that no one else should see him, so that Mum on some level couldn't really believe it until his clothes were returned some time later.

Mum had to tell me that Eric was dead, and I didn't really understand what that meant. Certainly as a boy I could have had no understanding of the turning point this was to be in our lives.

We could never be sure how his death happened. It could have been a true accident – a fall as he hunted a rabbit; there was a branch that he might have tripped on. But there was always a nagging doubt. He'd just started boarding school that year and he didn't like it. He'd asked to transfer to Marlborough Boys' as a day student, but Dad had said no. And now it was the end of the holidays and he was due to go back the following day. So there was always a feeling it could have been suicide.

Whatever the truth, it destroyed Dad. I heard the police yelling at him, calling him a useless bastard for letting his thirteen-year-old go out by himself with a gun. Dad blamed himself, and for the next four years he cried every day. He was a broken man. He was around forty years old, had a life history of service to the community, but he was broken. He withdrew from all his worldly involvements. He had been about to become a Justice of the Peace; he withdrew from that, telling Mum, 'They don't want criminals.'

We had an employee called Fred Jones who worked for us for thirty-five years, and it was not uncommon for Fred to find my father crying on the side of a hill, and he'd gather him up and bring him home to Mum. Mum became the rock that held our lives together. She just rolled up her sleeves and got on with it, supported by her Christian faith. My father, though, lost his faith. Every night, as I lay

Dad wasn't a mainstream thinker, and he indoctrinated me to not be afraid to think differently.

in my bed, I heard him sobbing through the bedroom wall. It went on and on and on. He blamed himself and he couldn't forgive himself.

My brother Basil wrote a biography of our father, and in it he ponders this period of Dad's grief: 'Today, when I look back on that time now knowing vastly more about Graham's war experiences, my sense is that this loving and gentle little man was also consumed, underneath, by a more complex and maybe subconscious need for an emotional catharsis in the wake of the war. Perhaps here it was, triggered by Eric's death, prolonging the whole grieving period?'

Imagine if that's true – the brutal effect of the war on that whole generation of men who served and came back.

I was now the only child at home. I still had two years before going to boarding school. My older brother and sister returned as little as possible because it was such an awful environment.

Four years my father spent in hell, with at least two suicide attempts; and then, amazingly, it was Wendy's father, Ted Loe, who helped him recover. He came round one day and told Dad he was forming a Lions Club in the district, and would Dad like to join? To that moment, Dad had the view that he was just a useless waste of space and had no value to the world, and was constantly suicidal, and somehow Ted hit the mark. He convinced Dad that joining something like that would be a good thing, and that was the beginning of the next phase of Dad's life. His next forty years were spent as a servant of humankind – different from before, but just as giving – and through serving others, he saved himself.

I always appreciated that, despite his pain and horror at my brother's death, Dad never tried to wrap me in cotton wool. How the hell he coped with watching me, I don't know. Eric's death never restricted me in my own personal development – I never felt any greater sense of mortality. I always thought I knew what I was doing. I didn't, of course, but I was a young bloke and I thought I knew everything.

4

STANDING ON MY OWN

The tail lights of my parents' car grew smaller as it headed away. They were bright points of red – then they vanished around a curve in the long driveway. I sat on the big wooden seat at the front of Nelson College's Barnicoat House – the boarding house where I was to live for the next four years – and had a bit of a cry. I suddenly realised I was being weaned.

I'd always wanted to come here, to Nelson College, like my brothers before me. Eric, of course, was no longer here. Basil had finished in 1966, but he'd been a prefect and his name lived on. But much as I'd looked forward to it this moment was hard. Then I was joined on the seat by a large Niuean, a bit older than me.

'Hey, mate,' he said. 'Are you okay?'

'Yeah, I'm fine,' I told him, sniffing and trying to wipe my tears away.

'What's your name?'

I told him, mumbling through my tears and snot.

'Any relation to Bas?'

'He's my brother.'

'He's a good guy,' this large fellow said. He added kindly, 'Do you want to come up the hill for a smoke?'

So within about two minutes of being dropped off at Nelson College I was up the hill behind the school, trying my first cigarette. It just about killed me. The Niue islander who took me there was Toke Talagi, who is now the premier of Niue, and was appointed Knight Companion of the New Zealand Order of Merit in 2017. He's about three years older than me, and he went on to be a really outstanding member of the Barnicoat House community and a prefect.

Apart from that first moment of sadness, I absolutely loved my time at Nelson College. For the first time, I loved the academic side of school. Primary school had prepared me so poorly I ended up in the B band at Nelson, where in nearly every subject I fought to be in the top one or two. I went through three years in that B band and got the highest School Certificate marks of anyone in our hostel, and that wasn't done by academic excellence – but by sheer hard work. I was lucky to be among a group of people who all wanted to do better than they had in the past and we all spurred each other on. Because of my good grades I was put up into the A band for my sixth-form year, and it was a good thing I wasn't there earlier because I found it really hard – the speed at which the class was moving was faster than my capability.

Rugby was a major part of school life – did I mention the rugby? At primary school it has been played every break and every winter weekend. We had an okay team and every year, right from my first year playing, I got in the age-graded Marlborough Rep team, which was great because it showed me the next level. I learned that there were levels in life and I really enjoyed feeling the benefit of playing at that higher level.

Preparing me for Nelson College, my parents had instructed me to involve myself in everything I could. I gave cricket a go in that first summer term and I was hopeless. I couldn't wait to toss it, but my parental training was to always see things through.

At the first sign of cooler weather, my time arrived: the trials for sixth-grade rugby. I played a beaut and rushed to the noticeboard to see the selected teams. As I had hoped, I made the 6A team, and we went on to thrash all opponents. I had never played with such a classy lot and it was great to be with guys who were all so good at their job. Our closest game that season was 24 to 3 against Waimea College.

Next year the same thing – selected for the fifth-grade A team. Another wonderful year of rugby and much of the same team.

But in the fifth form, things changed. My maths teacher was the selector for the fourth-grade A team. He and I didn't get along. I'm still certain I put in the best open-side flanker performance at the trial, but when I turned up to the noticeboard I was in the B team. It was a great shock to me and I took it really personally. The B team was a good side but of far lower ability.

My friend Simon Wall was also in the B team. When it came time to play the A team in competition Wall and I rallied the guys like never before. We went out and beat them. This was unprecedented and got an ovation in assembly on Monday morning. The second round came and the return game was played on the main field with a huge number of students turning up to back us underdogs. Once again, Wall and I pumped the team up and they played like men possessed and we won.

To this day, that event has left an impact on my determination under fire. The As beat us in the competition overall, but we'd shown them two very substantial games. Maths classes took on renewed satisfaction and that teacher was never to coach a top team in the college again.

In a way I feel a little sad about this story – I'm embarrassed about how determined I became on that occasion. That teacher had deeply hurt me, but I still feel bad at the lengths I went to show him up. Long-term, however, it taught me a lot about working a team and driving a vision. I learned to trust my ability to move men, and it gave me the power of self-belief. The next year, my trial for the top 3A team was successful.

In my fourth and final year at Nelson I had one of my favourite teachers for maths, David Nightingale – but sadly my maths still languished.

Life at Nelson College was like an amazing book that was opening to me and I took on many other things – I learned clarinet and this time enjoyed my musical experience. I sang in choirs, loved running, and in the fifth form I found another of my enduring loves.

Nelson College's Mataki Lodge had recently been built in the Mataki Valley, west of Nelson Lakes National Park. It was where the school based its outdoor education programme, and it's where I developed my absolute love of the mountains of New Zealand. I did a leadership course there at the end of the fifth form and was able to take groups in the mountains. At the end of my sixth-form year I spent six weeks up there. That love carried through into my married life when Wendy and I took our kids all over New Zealand, tramping the major walks.

In that sixth-form year my parents went for an extended tour of Europe, and while they were away I became very unsettled and wanted to leave school. When they returned, Dad was great at working it all through with me. He never told me to stay: just gave me the choice, but pointed out that I was so near to completion. It was crafty counselling on his part. If he'd ordered me to stay I would have left like a shot. In the end, I finished the year and was accredited University Entrance. Dad really knew how to manage a sometimes very stroppy boy.

The school urged me to stay for a seventh-form year and leadership roles; Dad urged me to go to Lincoln College (as it was then called), the agricultural university – but neither of those appealed. All I wanted was to come back home to the farm and get my hands dirty.

5

EXCITEMENT GALORE

I knew I wanted to farm. But truth to tell, I really left school because Dad was still struggling so badly. The whole time I was at Nelson College I was aware he could hardly drag his broken self around life. When I came home for the holidays his mental state lifted; he loved having me home, and I thought coming home might help him. I was excited to think I'd add value to the place, to his life.

But Dad already had his man, Fred Jones, working for him, and it was in those days still only a small farm. There wasn't really room for me. Dad put me on to grubbing thistles – days, weeks, months of it – and I grew increasingly frustrated. Eventually I thought, I didn't choose this life to do this kind of work. I was getting paid, yet there was no meaningful reward in it for me.

I had a discussion with Dad. 'You've got to learn that you start off at the bottom of the tree,' he said. Well, the bottom of the tree was too far down for me. I told him I didn't want to work at home any more.

I went to the next-door neighbour, who I knew was short of workers, and asked if I could help. 'Yeah,' he said, 'yeah, I'd love you to come and work for me.'

'When can I start?' I asked.

'Now,' he replied.

I asked how much he'd pay me and when he told me I thought, hell, that's so much higher than what I've been getting at home. I shot home and told Dad I'd got a job and he said, 'Good.'

'By the way,' I said, 'I'm getting quite a bit more money.'

'You didn't use to pay board,' he pointed out. 'You'll have to pay board now. How much extra did you get?'

I told him and he said, 'That'll all go on board.'

Even today, I laugh when I think about that conversation. It was fair enough. I started at the neighbouring farm and I absolutely loved it. The place was a mess and things were chaos but I was that farmer's main man. He had me ploughing and fencing, making silage, driving the tractors – all the jobs I was born and bred to do. They were endless and very fulfilling. I really felt like I was contributing. Soon I was given the task of painting all the sheds. Some were so rotten the brush tore away the wood. I was just wasting my time but, employed by the hour, I kept brushing.

I'd only been there a few months when I came home one day and Dad said, 'You'll lose your job shortly. The place you're working at is for sale.'

'We've got to buy it,' I said immediately. *Opportunity*. I don't know how I knew it, but it was what I was looking for.

'I don't want to buy that place. It's a rundown heap of rubbish,' Dad said.

I convinced him he needed to go and have a look. It was no use. 'I'm even less interested now,' he said, once he'd looked over the property. It was covered in manuka – which in those days we called 'scrub' – the woolshed was had it, the fences were had it, the pastures were had it. Everything was had it. But where Dad could see hard work and unwanted debt, I saw nothing but opportunity. A week went by as he refused to be interested and I sweated. Finally I dragged him back up there again, and we sat on a hill looking out over the expanse of the two farms together – Bonavaree was 206 hectares, and this second farm, Glen Erin, was 450. If we were to buy Glen Erin it would nearly triple our holding.

'Dad,' I said, 'let's dream what it might be like with our touch.'

He listened. My father had high ability in farming; he'd just burnt out with the process of life. But he could see he had a really high-energy life form on his hands, one that needed calming down by a bit of hard work. So he said, 'If I buy it you've got to stay home and work it.'

'You've got a deal,' I said. And the upshot was he applied for funds to buy that farm, and the sale went through. Takeover day was set for 1 February 1973.

That day, that deal – it was probably the thing that kept me interested in farming and it set me off in a model of investment and growth that seemed to work well, right up until the mid-1990s. Dad paid for it at the beginning, but I pushed the whole thing, created the opportunity to build the platform that is Bonavaree today.

He told me later that he didn't sleep for the first three months after signing the purchase deal, he was so worried about the debt we'd taken on. He'd taken on very little debt in his whole life.

Dad put me in charge of Glen Erin, and in no time at all I was living the dream, taking a rundown place and making it good. He caught the excitement, found a whole new gear, and the next six years were wonderful. He and Fred Jones looked after Bonavaree and I ran the new block with a young guy I employed as farm hand, Michael McKee. We worked hard and long hours and young Michael was my style – competitive and physical.

Dad put me in charge of Glen Erin, and in no time at all I was living the dream, taking a rundown place and making it good. He caught the excitement, found a whole new gear, and the next six years were wonderful.

Nineteen seventy-three. There can hardly have been a more momentous year in the history of farming in this country. First there was the oil shock – the price of oil skyrocketed, hugely increasing the cost of transport and dragging the price of imports upwards as a result. And then Britain, which had been by far our major market, joined the European Common Market, effectively ending its old export agreement with us. It's hard to overstate the impact that had on New Zealanders. At the same time, the United States, a major market for our beef, made changes to its import formula that made life tougher for New Zealand farmers.

Successive New Zealand governments stepped in to help bolster the farming industry, and the subsidies began to fly. First Labour's Norman Kirk introduced subsidies for fertiliser, and waived interest on loans to farmers. Then after 1975, National's Robert Muldoon really started to crank it up. Subsidies were increased – crazy schemes that paid a dollar for every sheep on your farm on 1 July were introduced. So we lambed early and counted every one. In addition, supplementary minimum prices were put in place to anchor farmers' returns for meat and wool.

This led to significant growth in livestock numbers, with the number of sheep nationwide reaching seventy million in the early 1980s. We produced huge amounts of meat for which there was no market, and real prices fell. By the late 1970s the country had a stockpile of sheep meat. By the early 1980s, government support for agriculture was equivalent to thirty per cent of the total output from farming.

Farmers were paid through cheap land development loans to clear marginal land of scrub to grow grass, meaning large tracts of land were developed that should never have been touched. The subsidies were capitalised into land prices and unaffordable wages and costs.

All those subsidies protected farmers from the realities of the world. History would show this was the craziest time in local farming history. Every signal we got was born from the wrong reasoning. Kirk and Muldoon: together they took New Zealand agriculture to its knees.

We would sit and watch the Budget on TV to see how much money we were going to make. The finance minister was our golden feeder. Dad was a wise man; he told me: 'Make sure we spend the money on production, as this won't last.' A lot of farmers went and bought a new car and that contributed to the underlying problem, because while the fellow at the car sales yard made a buck, it didn't underpin our export wealth. At Bonavaree and Glen Erin, we kept very focused on increasing our own performance.

One of the lasting ramifications of that period has been that, socially, a massive change occurred in how farmers were viewed. Subsidies returned the taxpayer very little, and public opinion became severe; the general public hated the amount of money that had been spent on subsidisation, which produced absolutely nothing for the well-being of this nation. We went from being called the 'backbone' of the country to the 'wishbone'. People gloated when subsidies were ripped away virtually overnight by the Labour government in 1984, and many farmers went to the wall. The public profile of agriculture has never recovered from this time and many Kiwis still look at us as bludgers.

Lessons learned through this time served me well for the rest of my farming life.

Back in early 1973, as we began our new venture, that turmoil still lay ahead. All I knew was that remodelling Glen Erin was everything I'd dreamed about. We hit the ground running. A severe drought gripped eastern Marlborough and the farm had very little feed. That very first week we sold half of the 1200 ewes we'd purchased, receiving double the price we paid in the deal. We thus freed up some good grazing land for our Bonavaree cows.

We poured labour and materials into the place – we had trucks coming in with new fencing materials, with building materials for new sheds; trucks going out with our produce. We were not only enjoying the revenues we were unlocking from that land, we were learning about economies of scale. Essentially, we had changed our business model. My grandfather and father happily and successfully farmed Bonavaree under the old family farm model, where everyone had their little block to keep their own family. Now I'd introduced a model of investment and growth. For me, it was excitement galore.

I was seventeen when we took over Glen Erin – already a year out of school. I worked hard and played hard. I banked all my salary to buy shares in the farm. For my entertainment and courting money, I grew a few little pigs and sold them for cash. With that I bought dance tickets and beer. There would be a lot of older guys around the community who remember me from that time. They rolled their eyes when they saw me with my long hair and my scruffy appearance, chasing their daughters.

6

LOVE ON THE FLAXBOURNE

I was up on the Kaka Plateau – the highest point of our farm – not long ago with a friend. It was a beautiful day and up there was like being on top of the world. With the Kaikouras at our back, the view stretched right across to Wellington. We could even – just – see the wind turbines on the hills above Makara, and then we could turn and look south down the coast towards Kaikoura. We were taking in the glorious view when this guy said, 'So whereabouts did Wendy come from, Doug?'

'See those trees down over there?' I replied, pointing. 'That house just behind those trees.'

'Oh, you married somebody local?'

'Yeah, yeah, I was pretty busy.'

'Where'd your mother come from?'

'Well, see those trees over there . . .' We had a good laugh.

Around the same time, I went along to a meeting run by the bank's rural team. There was a family from Nelson and another from Blenheim, and the rest were just people from around here, including my cousin, my mother's sister's son, who lives just over the back of my farm.

'Now, ladies and gentlemen,' the facilitator said, 'we'll get this day under way and I'll start round here on this side of the table. Could you introduce yourself and tell us how you fit in here.'

One of the guys hopped up and said, 'My name's Malcolm Taylor and I farm at Ward. This guy here, Doug Avery, is my first cousin. His wife's related to that couple over there, that's Kevin and Carol Loe, and this couple over here, that's Doug's daughter and her partner Lochy is my cousin. As far as I can establish,' he said, to lots of laughter, 'it's all above board.'

Of course I always knew who Wendy was – she was the 'little girl Loe' who had her piano lesson in the time slot before me – and our families knew each other; but Wendy and I didn't really know each other. However, it wasn't long after I started farming at Glen Erin that we ran into each other. We were eighteen when we met.

I was whitebaiting with a friend on the Flaxbourne River. We were having a few beers and the whitebait weren't much in evidence, so we decided to block the whole stream. Unbeknownst to us, a couple of girls were whitebaiting further up the stream, and they decided to come down and find out why they weren't catching any all of a sudden. They gave us a bit of a word-up about us blocking the stream, but once they settled down and we got talking, one of them asked me if I'd give her a ride into Blenheim that night. 'Yeah,' I said, 'I can do that alright.' That was Wendy. I dropped her into town, and I asked her if she wanted to go with me to the Young Farmers' Ball in Picton. She said yes – and that was the start of the luckiest thing that ever happened to me.

Life with a farmer was not at all what Wendy had mapped out for herself. She'd grown up on her parents' farm, but of all her five sisters she was the only one who really hated that life. She couldn't wait to be a city girl, and had her eye on teachers' college. But we fell in love. Then I told her that if she moved away, that was our relationship over, and so she stayed. I proposed, and we got married in 1976; we were both twenty-one. She found she loved farming. It's different when it's your own place, when you're building your own riches and your own dreams.

We slogged it out together at Glen Erin for those first years. Fraser was born in 1979, followed by Alice in 1981 and Richard in 1986. For all those years, when the children were little, Wendy was very involved with the farm, very hands-on. The kids went in the backpack while she was tailing lambs, or there'd be a baby in the pram and one on her back, and another playing in among the lambs.

Her friend that she was whitebaiting with that first day had been more of a farm girl when they were younger, but she ended up in Auckland, and she used to write to Wendy saying, 'I can't believe you're living in among shitty little lambs.'

We built our business together, every step forward meaning sacrifice.

In 1979 I began to think about where we were headed. The purchase of Glen Erin, which had given Dad sleepless nights at the start, had turned into his best ever financial decision. His net worth, over the years since that purchase, had increased beyond all belief, but of course that put Wendy and me in a bad place. We needed to act quickly, or our goal of ownership would become unachievable. I asked Dad what was happening with the farm.

'Can I buy it?' I asked.

'Give me a month,' he said. He approached my brother and sister to see if they were interested in being involved in Bonavaree, which they both declined. So the property was valued and we bought the place. My parents left fifty per cent of the capital in at a relatively low interest rate which I paid back in full over the years, and the rest we paid through raising capital from the bank. My parents paid my brother and sister out and were able to buy a retirement home in Blenheim. Wendy and I were twenty-six when we fully took over Bonavaree. Mum and Dad moved into town in 1982, and at that point we moved from the Glen Erin house back to the house I grew up in, at Bonavaree.

It's been a real partnership, Wendy and me; yet I don't think I truly appreciated Wendy until she got breast cancer and I started to think about what life would be like without her. I don't think I've ever not appreciated her since. Now, when we go to the city, she loves it for a very short time, but soon wants to be home again. 'It's just not me, living in the rat race,' she says.

We were extremely lucky with our timing. When the government, with no warning, abolished all subsidies in 1984, a sizeable part of our income disappeared overnight, with the stroke of a pen. Farmers went cold turkey. Those who had less of a start than us, and also the support industries, really took a bath, and there was immense anger among rural folk.

Unlike many, I did not think it was wrong for the government to remove subsidies, but it did hurt very badly and left us unsure of what to do. I didn't handle it emotionally particularly well. If that's the way the country wants to treat me then I won't work hard any more, I thought. I'll work for myself and I'll do cash jobs.

However, we slashed costs and moved to self-sufficiency. We bought a milk cow and we just worked to feed ourselves. I challenged all my suppliers as to their costs and moved my business to new people when the old ones failed to accommodate my new-found poverty.

I had found the great truth: easy-earned money was easy to spend, and with hard-earned dollars I made sure to get maximum value out of everyone.

7

SNATCHED IN A MOMENT

Farmers, in their hearts, accept that they've got a pretty dangerous job. We all know somebody that's been killed on the job. My first employee died under a tractor here the first day Wendy and I got back to the farm after our honeymoon. It happened before my eyes. Scars. I'm full of scars.

Michael McKee was a local boy. He left school the day he turned fifteen; he'd hated school, loved the farming life. He worked for me for three years and by the time of the accident he was only eighteen. He was a terrific worker and a good friend. We used to race each other when we were crutching, just to see who could do the most. He had the edge on me.

In the weekends he used to go out in his Mark III Zephyr with a hotted-up motor in it. One time I was coming home from town, I was probably doing a hundred, and he shot straight past me. I used to think, you mad bugger, and I'd say to him, 'Slow down.' But that wasn't what killed him. He just made an error and it wasn't a big one. He wasn't drunk, he wasn't being stupid and he wasn't showing off. He failed to remember to do one thing and that was enough to finish his life.

We had a brand-new tractor, a Same Corsaro; it was our first four-wheel-drive tractor. He used it while I was away, so on that first morning back I asked: 'What do you want to do? Drench sheep or go and do some tractor work?'

'I'd really like to do the tractor work,' he said, so I let him go.

He did a great job, but when he was coming in for lunch he decided to take this new tractor out the side of the hill. I was working in the yard, saw him coming and thought, holy hell, what's he coming that way for? And I immediately saw his mistake. He hadn't lowered the front-end loader.

This new tractor had a massive six-foot bucket on it and he had it right up in the air. As I watched, the tractor tipped over. I saw him flung from the seat, landing below the tractor, which by this time was upside down, held up by the safety frame and the arms of the front-end loader – and then, as I watched, down it all came on top of him.

I dropped what I was doing and sprinted across the paddock. The tractor was still running, had come through a fence and was sitting as if nothing had happened, shiny and new. At that moment, it had just sixteen hours on its clock. Young Michael lay dead beside it.

I had never seen a dead person before. Life seemed to move in slow motion. I ran to ring for help and to break the terrible news to Wendy, who had her first-ever lunch as a farmer's wife all prepared: asparagus and bacon – we never got to eat it.

I rang his family and his father came straight round. Then next day I got a ring and it was his father, asking me to come to their house. A hearse carrying Michael arrived and his casket was carried into the lounge. The whole family was gathered but the father insisted I see Michael first. Just he and I went into the room. 'There he is, Doug,' he said to me. 'I want you to see he is at peace. He is with our Lord.'

I couldn't believe the man's strength, to stand by his deceased eldest son, worrying about comforting me. For years he'd ring my father and ask, 'Is Doug okay?'

Our fortnight's honeymoon was the first time I'd ever really taken a break. We came home to a funeral and to a new realisation – that life can be snatched, just like that. It's something that farming people know only too well.

Wendy's introduction to married life was a man who woke every night from terrible nightmares, thinking something was falling on him, on her, crushing us to death. For a long time I didn't know how to cope with the trauma of seeing someone die. All I kept thinking was, what could I have done? What didn't I do to prevent that? I didn't know what I could do to put it right – and then, one day, I realised I couldn't. I just had to move on.

8

THE MIDDLE YEARS

Fraser, our first child, arrived in 1979, the same year we bought the farm from Mum and Dad. His birth was one of the most amazing experiences for me. I felt we had created the most special thing I had ever seen. He was born in the early hours of the morning and I wanted to tell the world. I rang Wendy's parents, who were staying in a hotel in Christchurch. I was stunned they seemed so unimpressed, until I worked out they were still half asleep. By about six-thirty I had made my way as far as Seddon, banging on the door of one of my mates to tell him of the arrival of this amazing son. They, too, were sound asleep, and all the banging in the world could not allow me to tell the world of my happiness.

Next day I bought some trees and planted them to mark the occasion. This act was later to catch up on me when the two younger children, Alice and Richard, asked: 'What trees did you plant when we were born?'

'Oh dear . . . none . . .'

Alice was born two years later. Richard followed in 1987, but sadly between Fraser and Richard, Wendy suffered four miscarriages. Each one created highly disheartening times and a couple of them seriously challenged her health.

On one occasion she was hospitalised for some time and I became chief carer. I was very keen to do the job well. I remember taking Alice to a playgroup one day dressed in her No. 1s, a smocked frock. This really threw all the other mothers right out of play with me, turning up with an overdressed child. I loved this time but was totally ready to hand back the household reins to Wendy when she regained her health, and I returned to my life as an extremely well-kept man.

These were the years of growing children, and Wendy and I jumped enthusiastically into community activities. When Fraser started school at Seddon – and, incidentally, all three kids loved their time there, the school having improved a lot since my day – I went onto the school committee. When Tomorrow's Schools (Labour's sweeping educational reform programme) was implemented in 1989, I became the first treasurer of Seddon's board of trustees, and then its chair. I loved this work and learned a lot about business administration and policy writing. My greatest contribution to that school was computer technology. I was a very early adopter, the third Marlborough farmer to acquire a computer, and the secretary and the principal all joined me on the journey of learning around computer use.

All our children were good at sport. I was soon coaching Fraser at rugby, but after two years of playing, his age group could not make a team so he took up hockey instead. He straight away made the rep hockey team, and our lawn became the practice paddock as Fraser passed on all his skill to the family. That led the other two to rep honours in hockey, and next thing, to our great joy, we were travelling all over New Zealand to tournaments with our children.

As they grew we began taking them on family mountain hikes. 'You should shout your kids a decent holiday,' people used to say to us, but I just used to think, you don't understand the dynamics we've developed as a family. Sometimes we'd be out on the ridge and there'd be wind or snow and I'd look at the kids and think, far out, this is good for you. Together, we did many of the main tracks around New Zealand.

I got Fraser, as the eldest, to carry the tent to slow him down and keep him under control. Richard would carry his sleeping bag and lollies. I can remember him suddenly sitting down as we were slogging across the Hollyford face of the Routeburn Track. It was stinking hot, and he'd had enough. 'I've had it,' he said. 'You go on without me. You just go on.' He was seven. He's now thirty and an ultrarunner; in 2016 he beat the Western Australia ultrarunning record with 240.431 kilometres in twenty-four hours.

So I believe those holidays were hugely formative. We tented at Totaranui in the Abel Tasman for two weeks every year, with no electricity or hot water, even when the children were tiny.

They were busy years, but filled with good things. I tell you all this so that you'll understand the contrast between those years of energy and optimism, and what happened to me during the long drought.

We recovered from the removal of subsidies, and got back to thinking broadly after a period of clamping down. It wasn't long before we were again looking to expand Bonavaree. We signed an offer on a property in Tetley Brook, the next valley north-west of our farm. It suddenly struck us that we'd offered too much, and the property wasn't right, so about an hour later I rang the real estate agent.

'How long before I can withdraw the offer?'

'You can't,' he said.

We had an anxious few weeks, but thankfully the offer was turned down. *Phew* – that was close. However, word got out that we were looking to expand, and our Grassmere neighbours Tom and Susanne Jeffries approached us to see if we wanted to lease their properties. A couple of days later we had written a lease document and signed it all up, and we were driving the Jeffries' property.

This move led to the start of dairy grazing, which in some years has made up one-third of our income. We took on some more capital stock, but put dairy heifers on about half of the new property. We poured the fertiliser on and ramped up production.

About a year into the lease the Jeffries approached us saying they wished to sell the property. We were keen to buy it, but said it would be better for us if it was a year later. I'll never forget Mrs Jeffries pointing out to us that in life we always think next year will be better. 'Doug,' she said, 'do you want to buy it or not?'

Wendy and I went to the Jeffries' home to hear what they wanted for the property. 'Don't show any emotion when they reveal the price,' I said to Wendy. 'We will hear it and leave to absorb.'

The asking price was huge. I knew there was no way I could justify the price or even raise the money; we drove home stunned.

However, there was another neighbouring property likely to come on the market, owned by Henry Gluyas, so I went to see him. I was open about the fact we were negotiating with the Jeffries, but asked what he'd want for his farm. He told me, and it was the right price, the fair price.

Back I went to the Jeffries to inform them of the situation. I would be happy to step away from the lease and allow them to sell to someone else if I was successful in concluding the Gluyas deal, I said. Early next morning, Tom Jeffries rang. 'I want you to come back to the table,' he said. So back we went. 'What would you pay?' the Jeffries asked us. I wrote down the sum, pushed it across to them, and they accepted.

'We will let the lawyers do the work now,' Tom said. We shook hands and for me the deal was done, subject to finance.

That night I hardly slept. Should we extend and buy both? It was tempting. Because we had already spent so much on the Jeffries property, we wanted it the most; but was there a chance we could really push and buy both?

Just one, Doug, I eventually told myself. It was a good call, as history has shown that buying two could have been enough to tip us over the edge when the hard times came.

Purchasing from neighbours can sometimes be very difficult, but we've been lucky to work with honourable people in our land-buying processes. The Jeffries were long-term family friends – as, in fact, were the Gluyases – and my grandfather had passed many hours playing chess with Tom's father, Merv Jeffries. Some time after the purchase of the property I found Merv Jeffries' 1922 diary. Nearly every day he recorded: 'Avery arrived about 2 p.m. and we played chess all afternoon.' Occasionally he would write, 'Avery came up and helped me fencing.'

Purchase by purchase, from Glen Erin in 1973, to the Jeffries' farm in the post-subsidy world of 1993, the biggest learning for me was of the power of scale. Every time we bought a farm or leased a farm, the running costs went up only a little as we utilised our equipment better. We increased mob size to achieve better paddock grazing, hence requiring less stockman's work per unit of production. And we only had one end-of-year set of accounts to do.

If you'd asked me then, I might have said the good times would go on for ever. I felt like a man in control of his life.

We were adjusting to the new challenge of what my accountant once called 'living in the real world'. As ever, I was excited to adapt to that world, but I never realised how many people would stay in a totally protected environment while farmers, and a small group of others, faced this big world alone.

Meanwhile, the 'real world' was about to hit us from another direction.

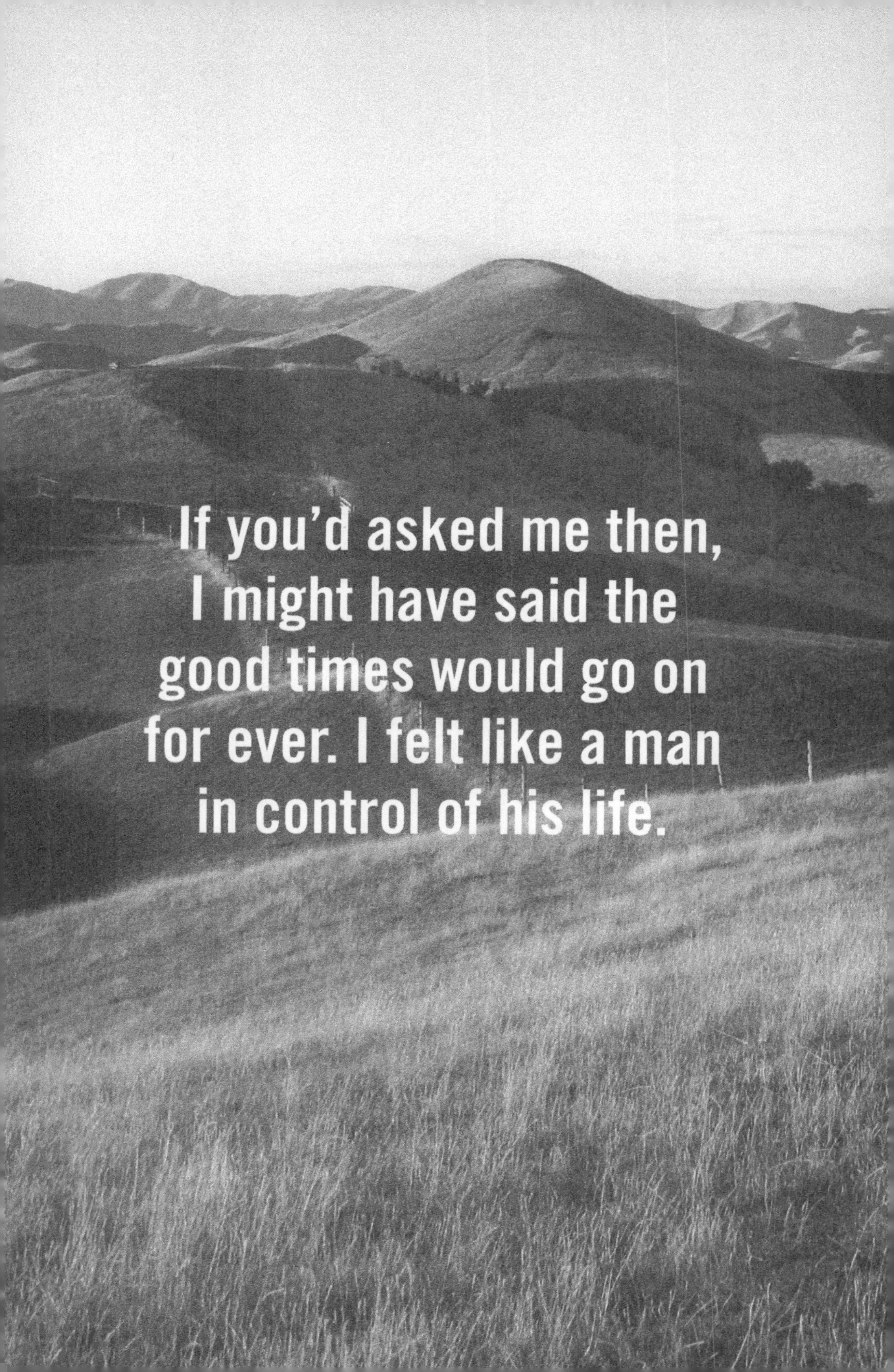

If you'd asked me then, I might have said the good times would go on for ever. I felt like a man in control of his life.

9

THE REAL WORLD

That same year, Wendy found a lump in her breast. I gave little thought to the possibility it could be bad. She was so well, and only in her thirties! But she went to the doctor and it wasn't long till the phone rang. Wendy answered, and I saw her face drop.

It hit us hard. Cancer – we couldn't even say the word. We had to wait six weeks for Wendy's preferred surgeon to come back from holiday, and it was a terrible six weeks of uncertainty and fear.

We struggled. One of Wendy's sisters took the children down to Christchurch for a week, and Wendy and I went to Hanmer. That would be good, we thought: we'd had so many lovely times there. But the cancer came with us and nothing seemed right. It was an early lesson in the worthlessness of running away. When you pack your bags, you pack your problems along with the rest of your gear.

We talked and talked between ourselves but we couldn't say that dreaded word to other people. Wendy was approached by a friend to see if she could help cater an event, and Wendy couldn't find the words to say, 'Look I won't be here, I'm going to be in hospital.' Instead, she just stared straight through her friend, who snapped, 'I'm not asking you for a million dollars, for goodness' sake. All I'm asking is for you to help.'

When she eventually learned the truth, that poor woman felt so bad that she organised six other women to come to the house after Wendy was back home, and they did a whole day in the garden. That was special.

After our long wait, we finally met with the surgeon and talked about what lay ahead. Immediately, we settled down; we knew what to expect, and suddenly Wendy knew she could cope. She's never looked back.

I took Wendy to Wairau Hospital for a mastectomy, delivering her to a stark hospital ward. The next day when I returned the room was so full of flowers I could hardly find her. The nurse said she had never seen such an outpouring of love.

Some time later, Wendy took a counselling training course through the Cancer Society, and for years she counselled other women diagnosed with breast cancer. She'd get a call, usually from the surgeon who had just made the diagnosis, and she would meet with women before their surgery. She loved helping them, and she travelled with them right through their journey.

No one is the same after they've been through a cancer experience. Wendy will tell you it made her appreciate every moment of every day. It made her feel, *Look, I don't have to answer to anybody. If I want to do something I will do it.*

One day she had taken her lunch to eat outside under a favourite tree. It was a lovely day and so she stayed out there a while, reading a book. Up the drive came a stock agent. He looked at her and said, 'Caught!'

Wendy bristled. 'I don't have to justify sitting here reading to you or anybody.'

He looked a bit surprised, but there's no point feeling guilty about simply enjoying the day, enjoying the peace, taking time to rest in a busy day. Life's too short.

Wendy will also tell you that going through cancer was nothing compared with having to live with me through my bad time, when I became a bitter, blaming man. But that was still three years in the future, and 1993 hadn't finished with us yet.

Our daughter Alice was fading away before our eyes. She was an excellent sports player, constantly challenging her own set levels of excellence in sport and school. Yet nothing could disguise the fact that she was losing strength. We had countless trips to the doctor before at last a sugar test confirmed she had diabetes. I'll never forget watching our little girl load a needle of insulin and shake and cry as she built up the courage to inject. She would not accept help, but in no time at all was in control of her life again.

As the year rolled on I was just settling in to the fact my girls were all back on track when I got a phone call to say Dad was in intensive care at Wairau Hospital. He'd had a cardiac arrest in the street.

I raced to Blenheim and found a gently smiling father lying in bed, wired up to various pieces of equipment.

'He's very lucky,' the doctor said. 'When emergency crews arrived a young boy was doing CPR. Without that he would be gone.'

'Who was the boy?' I asked.

No one knew, but I shot straight round to the place where Dad had fallen. There was no sign of anything or anyone, so I went to a house on the other side of the road where a woman was working in her garden.

'Did you see anything strange around here today?' I asked.

'Oh,' she said, 'a man died over there.' She pointed to the spot. 'A kid was jumping on him and I told him to stop.'

'Do you know who the kid was?' I asked.

He was the son of the hairdresser in Redwoodtown, she told me. So I was off to Redwoodtown. Alan Gibbons was the hairdresser there and it was fourteen-year-old Brady who had saved our dad. It was an incredible story. Brady was being driven home from soccer practice by his father when he saw Dad collapse. 'Stop the car,' he told his father. 'There's a man in trouble.' He had learned CPR at Sea Scouts a couple of years before, so he knew what to do. Others, much older than Brady, tried to stop him from assisting Dad, but he was backed up by a young woman who ordered the small crowd back and helped Brady while he did the chest compressions.

Young Brady was such a hero to us. He displayed the courage to act, even when popular opinion was against him. Dad supported him to take a cycle tour to the USA, and it was little wonder to me that he eventually graduated from Victoria University with honours in architecture. After Dad died eleven years later, we awarded Dad's Distinguished Flying Cross to Brady. Dad had received the DFC for courage and devotion to duty; Brady had earned that medal when he saved our father. He wore it with pride to an Anzac service with his grandfather, whom our mother, Joyce, had nursed back to wellness at Wairau Hospital after he was shot up at Monte Cassino. 'I always knew we would get a chance to repay your family,' Brady's grandfather told us.

My whole life has been like this. Amazing things happen when we act with courage, generosity and gratitude. Out of those qualities we form connection and pride, and our lives are altered and the world changes just a bit.

As I look back over those years, it's clear now that I had no idea what huge changes lay in wait. If you'd asked me then, I would have predicted that I'd go on farming in much the same way as before, with good years and bad years, until I handed the farm over to someone else. I couldn't have predicted the crisis that was going to shake me like a housewife shaking a rug. And yet, I think now that 1993 in particular, when we went through so much that was emotionally challenging, may have been the beginning of my broken time. I wasn't yet in crisis, but, like so many people, I just limped on, maybe a bit grimmer, maybe a bit quicker to anger than I had been. Perhaps I had unwittingly wandered a bit close to the cliff edge but, in the fog of everyday life, hadn't realised it.

I didn't, in those days, have the understanding or the language even to think about such things. But when the real crisis hit, it was the push that sent me over the cliff.

PART TWO

10

A BROKEN MIND CAN'T DIAGNOSE A BROKEN MIND

Where's the wealthiest place in the world? Where's the most treasure buried? When I ask people that they throw place names around – Monaco? Beverly Hills? No. The answer is the graveyard. It's the graveyard because so many people have had a life but they haven't really lived it. They had a song in their head but they never sang it. They had a business but they were never prepared to let it flourish.

Their dreams, all the riches they wanted but never dared pursue, are buried with them.

I was definitely in danger of ending up like that. I was completely stuck. I'd stopped developing my life. I fell into what I now know was a serious depression.

I didn't realise that I suffered depression until ten years after I'd begun suffering it. I thought everyone else had turned ugly on me – and of course a depressed person can behave in a way where all they'll get is ugly reactions. I blamed everyone else at the time, but I now know that I was 100 per cent wrong. That's why depression is so serious: all the wrong people pay the price for what's going on.

Depression is not the same as stress. It's very different from the normal, fruitful stresses of life. Whatever your field of endeavour, if you want a successful life you'll never succeed if you're not prepared to expose yourself to some healthy stress. *God, I've got these timelines on me. I'm going to have to get up early tomorrow morning and do extra work . . .* A bit of stress is healthy, motivating, stimulating, and can make us very productive.

But depression is a different beast. It is a very deep valley that's almost impossible to climb out of under your own steam. If we don't know how to manage our healthy stress levels, if we don't cope well with the pressures life throws at us, our body's stress-response mechanism can become overactive. Stress that goes on for a prolonged period can mess with your body's chemical system and lead to depression.

The symptoms of depression are very different – almost opposite, in fact – to what you experience when you react to healthy stress. With depression, you're likely to feel hopeless, empty and tired all the time. You want to turn away from people, from the world. It all seems too much. And that feeling goes on and on.

It wasn't until life got good again that I realised what my problem was, and saw that what had become normal to me wasn't normal at all. That's why depression is such a tough bloody business, especially among men, because instead of talking to someone else, we merely self-diagnose. Self-diagnosis is all very well if you have a broken leg – you've got to be really, really stupid if you don't realise you've got a broken leg – but if you've got a broken mind it can be very hard to know there's a problem.

A broken mind can't diagnose a broken mind.

In the last few years as I've travelled all over the country sharing my story with other rural people, I have met countless depressed people. I only need to talk to somebody for a few minutes and I know. It's the eyes, the hollow eyes, that give it away. As if they've been hollowed out from the inside.

When I look at a person who's not suffering from depression, their eyes sparkle, and I can see they're engaged with the world. But with people who are in that dark place, it's almost as though their eyes are set back another quarter-inch. It's like they can't see where they're going – and they can't, actually. They can be so taken up with the ugliness and despair that's going on inside them, they can't look out at the world. It's too hard to confront the world; they want to withdraw.

Also, it's in the language they use. They tend to never say anything nice about themselves or anything else really, just default to negative all the time.

Farming communities tend to recognise this kind of behaviour only too well. That's not surprising, given the many stresses of farming. Statistics show that rural people are really suffering from depression and anxiety. Suicide – the extreme indicator – is higher among rural folk than in any other sector. In New Zealand we are twice as likely to die from our own hand as in a motor accident. Men are three times more likely to commit suicide than women, and rural men are twice as likely again. Climate change, tougher regulations, the economy, and the pressures of global markets all take a heavy toll. The suicide rate in rural Waikato became the highest in the country as international dairy prices halved during 2015–16.

But suicide, visible and horrifying, is just the tip of the iceberg. Below the surface is the giant, murky monsters of distress and depression.

I tackle these things head on, and try to use language and examples that come from the everyday of rural people's lives. I try not to use the word 'mental' – it freaks people out, and they immediately think of Jack Nicholson in *One Flew Over the Cuckoo's Nest*, strapped to a chair,

Depression is a different beast. It is a very deep valley that's almost impossible to climb out of under your own steam.

getting a lobotomy. If you put that word up there, most people in a dicey situation won't come to you. With the sort of people that I'm interested in helping, that word's not part of the discussion. Instead, we talk about being sad, or about the challenge of having issues in your head for a sustained period, and the risk of that.

It helps that I walk in their shoes, and that I'm like them. They see me up there, with my face and hands scoured and furrowed by our nor'westerlies, my voice gravelly from a lifetime of making myself heard against the bellowing of animals, in the wide open spaces that suck away the human voice and let us know on a daily basis how small we really are. I dress fairly smartly for these public events, but I might as well be wearing gumboots. I think they see me for what I am – one of them, a man of the land, who has struggled with the same things they're struggling with.

'Does anyone in the room know anyone who's had a broken arm or a broken leg?' I ask the sea of tired, exhausted faces. In every case nearly everybody puts a hand up. 'It's pretty bloody obvious, isn't it?' I say, 'because they stick out and they get caught in things and that.' People generally laugh then, and laughter is always good.

'So,' I say, 'that person that you know, when they broke their leg or their arm, did they leave it for a few months to see whether it needed treatment?' There's always a dead hush. *No*.

'I bet,' I say, 'that the moment it happened, the person was bailed into the ambulance or the car and you're straight to A and E, right?' *Yes*.

Then I ask another question. 'Does anyone here know anyone who, because of the pain of a broken leg or a broken arm, has taken their own life?' Their mouths drop a little at that idea, and no one raises a hand.

'So why,' I ask, 'do we leave a broken mind in the hope that it might come right? It's swinging in the wind – just like the leg would be – and the longer it's left the longer it can take to fix. And we all know' – and as farming folk, we really *do* know this – 'that people do take their own lives, out of the pain of a broken mind.'

Some people are more susceptible than others, maybe because of genetics or particular factors in their life situation. In my case, as well as the factors I've already described that rocked my universe, such as Wendy's cancer, our daughter's diabetes, and the prolonged drought, there was another indicator as well: a family history of depression. My grandfather Ern had experienced problems while my father, Graham, was away in the war. In many ways it was a logical response to the extremely dangerous job Graham was doing as the navigator of a Lancaster bomber, but Ern's symptoms went beyond normal stress and became something different. And then Graham himself, almost certainly traumatised by the war, took years to recover from the untimely death of my brother Eric. Graham's health over those years went far beyond 'ordinary' grief and definitely had the characteristics of severe depression.

So I was probably at reasonably high risk.

But there was another factor in there that was perhaps most dangerous of all: I was a man, of a certain generation, who had grown up in rural New Zealand in a culture that rarely ever talked directly about personal feelings. We didn't have the language. That's why, to me, the All Black John Kirwan is a hero because he gave us the language and the awareness, and he took away the shame and told us that depression is an illness, not a personal weakness. That's huge news in our culture where men in particular are encouraged to be the dominators, and not to show emotion.

But my dark days preceded John Kirwan's depression campaign, so all I had was my sense of personal failure, my fear and my blame.

My personal diagnosis, in those days, would have been that *the world is against me.* It wasn't until I accepted that I needed to change that I had any hope of getting better.

My mission now is to rob the graveyard of its wealth. To bury people who have left their best in their life, who have grown and released their excellence, rather than lived depressed and unfulfilled and taken all their potential to the grave.

11

MY JOURNEY DOWNWARDS

The sweetest fruits are on the outside branches. This is one of my favourite one-liners. When I was young I was full of courage and energy. I was climbing my tree, and I wasn't afraid to reach out and pick my fair share of fruit. I craved the rewards of hard work, of knowing my value in the world. I still do. But when things went bad for me I climbed down and became a trunk-hugger. I laid off my staff, I stopped spending money, I shut myself away from the world. I grabbed hold of the trunk of the tree and I held on for grim death.

But what can be found on a tree trunk? There is no fruit; there is no reward.

The early 1990s had been reasonably dry, but then 1995 was wet and we thought we were saved – saved, and justified for farming the way we did. But then 1996 was very dry and 1997 was terrible – the worst year on record, with just a drop or two over 300 millimetres. That was the year of the soul-destroying winds that sucked all water away from the land, taking our hope with it.

In the winter of 1998 it became obvious the drought yet again wasn't going to break. My accounts showed I'd earned $320,000 in revenue and spent $320,000 in running costs. That adds up to zero profit. The disappointment in myself was bitter and profound.

All my adult life, since taking over Glen Erin back in 1973, I'd told people I loved my business so much I didn't care whether I got paid. I felt like that right through to the 1990s until, suddenly, I wasn't getting paid. And then I realised I hated my business. By 1998, when the drought was doing to us big time and we were really facing the torch, I was in sheer hell. What I used to love doing, I could hardly bring myself to go and do. Everything was just a waste of time.

The spring rains that put water in the ground and in our dams and tanks failed, and again we were heading into summer unprepared, already depleted, no supplies.

Marlborough farmers know they farm in a dry district. They have old ways of coping with drought: reduce stock, bring in feed. A council water scheme was constructed after the 1958 drought, and this enabled farmers like me to carry stock in a way that previous generations had not been able to do, as it provided us with free drinking water for stock and for households. Before that, the old boys had to sell stock as dams and creeks dried out. No water, no stock. But in the late 1990s we still had water via the council scheme. So we farmers could go on providing for our stock even when the land had stopped providing.

I fought it the only way I knew how. I went down to Canterbury on a buying mission and spent around $40,000 on feed, and came back and fed it all out. It's a despairing scenario, the most emotionally destructive work I have ever done. Every sheep on the farm waits for its ration every day, as if each one is a friend; and as they rush after you, their feet tear up the land. You see your hope stripped away at the same time as you are exhausting your financial capital. You're praying for rain but you're just creating dust, to blow wherever that damn wind takes it.

One day a guy came down from the Manawatu looking to buy stock. I had a five-dollar price tag on my lambs and he looked me straight in the face and he said, 'Doug, I've got thousands to look at here today. Five dollars is way above my price; I'll give you a dollar.'

A dollar per lamb. I said thank you, and I loaded them on the truck. As he drove out the gate I was so grateful that he'd taken them off my hands. Those lambs crossed the Cook Strait and made the journey up to their new home, and about two days later a massive storm came through. I could see all the black clouds going up through there, and the Manawatu took an absolute hiding and every one of those lambs got washed into the Manawatu River and out to sea.

Anger and blame were weighing me down. The joys of the seasons, which had once been my greatest pleasures, became instead a misery. Autumn came and there was no rain, so we went into winter with everything still dry. The cold bit down, but when spring came there was not the usual relief: lambing began and we had no grass and the stress over feeding our stock just grew and grew.

We rolled on to summer full of fear. Instead of enjoying and relaxing in the heat, taking lazy afternoons off to enjoy the beach and each other, we were caught up in a desperate fight for survival. A sense of dread hung over every aspect of life. Autumn came and went again with no respite, and the hope that something would change yielded to yet more fear as winter approached. I began to fear that it would never come right – that I'd failed the land and the business and my legacy. It takes at least two generations to create a successful farm; only one to destroy it.

The uncertainty was the worst thing. If I have a flood or an earthquake or a massive windstorm or a death, I can see and feel immediately the quantum size of the problem. But with a drought there's no end, especially when it goes five years, six years, seven years, eight. Every day when you get up it's still there waiting for you.

In our lives as rural people, it's the land that's certain, and the seasons. Without those certainties, my core values floundered. Life was suddenly totally unrewarding. I had no financial reward, and no job satisfaction.

My knowledge band for creating a living out of this place didn't match the challenge of the weather systems that were rolling in, year after year. I'd got involved in farming when there was a bit of give on either side of the average-rainfall line, but I wasn't equipped for those years of drought. We got a big rainfall high in 1995, a real drenching; but ironically, looking back, I can see it made things worse. It distorted my perception of what I was up against. It gave me hope that our old ways were good ways; that I could carry on as before.

That year of rain we spent a fortune making surplus feed. I thought that if we made enough silage and hay, we could battle any drought. I didn't realise I had the mother of all droughts on my hands – the worst drought since 1890, when records began in this area. I still thought I was nature's master, and had yet to accept that the opposite is true: nature is our master. The process to discovering that took me to the very edge of my own emotional limits.

I feel certain that for change to happen, I had to break. The sweet fruits we eat today would never have been available to us if we had not been taken to the edge.

I was brought up to endure and then enjoy, to sow and then reap. These are the peaks and valleys of a normal life. As Sir James Wattie once said: 'The only place success comes before work is in the dictionary.'

12

HOLES IN THE WALL

Just get out of my life. I can't bear you close to me.

A depressed person can push other people away, and that's what I did. It happens because you've lost your confidence and you think it's easier to deal with this stuff without any other complications. You lose hope, and get angry easily. If anyone makes a mistake, you give them both barrels. That makes you feel good for a few seconds, but then you've done the damage.

I have a wonderful analogy. There's an angry man and he's lashing out at those around him, with no patience for anyone. A wise man watches this behaviour and decides to teach the angry man a lesson. He gives him a hammer and a box of nails. 'Every time you feel angry, drive a nail into the wall,' he tells him. The first day, the man drove about eight or ten nails in because he was so frequently angry, but as the days passed, he realised the futility of his anger and drove fewer and fewer nails into the wall.

'That's great,' the wise man said, 'you've slowed up. Now every day that you're not angry I want you to pull a nail out.'

So, over a period of time the man pulled all the nails out again. 'There,' he proudly said, 'all the nails are out.'

'Now look at the wall,' said the sage old adviser. 'You've pulled all the nails out and the nails are back in the box – but the holes are still in the wall. Once you punch those holes they will always be in the wall.'

When I was sad I shut down every opportunity that came my way. My wall was pitted with explosive responses to people. I'd get drunk at night – I drank from five o'clock until I was stuffed. When the phone went I'd answer and somebody would say something that I didn't think was appropriate, and before long I would have slagged them off.

I'd been the highest-polling candidate every time I stood for the board of trustees at Seddon School, and I ended up their chairman. But then Wendy got breast cancer and I was really struggling with that, and the weather began to be unreliable . . . and before I even realised what was happening inside me, I began to harbour this terrible anger.

One day a kid spat at the school cleaner, and in response she whacked the kid. That created a massive issue at the school. Many people were outraged at the cleaner, but I thought, if a kid spat at me I'd whack them too. Nobody spits at me and gets away with it. I felt so sorry for the cleaner, yet there was this massive outcry on the side of the kid. It all seemed too much, and instead of working my way calmly through the issue, I went to the board and I said, 'I can't stand it. I didn't join to put up with shit at this level. There's my resignation.'

A few weeks later I went to a Lions Club meeting, as I had done for eighteen years. Somebody shot some bloody stuff into me about something or other and I couldn't cope. I jumped out of the meeting, walked out, went home, wrote my resignation and sent it in. Shut myself away.

My father got a ring from one or two people after I burst out of the Lions meeting. *What the hell's the matter with Doug?* But he didn't know either, and he certainly never asked me about it. He wasn't that sort of fellow. We guys were never trained to be emotionally sharp, or to ask any personal questions. It wasn't done. Even though he never said anything, I know he worried. And there are still hundreds of men out there like that, but it's changing hugely, thank God.

Two months after that, the phone would go and I wouldn't even answer it. Wendy had to tell people I was out. I was so angry and disgusted at the whole world. I knew something was happening, but I didn't know *what* was happening; the truth is, my whole dream had fallen to bits.

Life's tough. Everyone's got a wall and there are holes in everybody's wall; some people have more than others. You can't take back what's done, but you can move forward.

Sometimes, even though Bonavaree is so successful and I'm well past my depression, I still feel a little of that fear. *What am I doing?* I ask myself. *I'm building this big thing; my dream is so huge . . . what happens if it happens again?* But then I remind myself that *at least I'm having a go*, and I'm not going to make the same mistakes again. I might make different mistakes, but I won't be blaming others for them, and I won't be isolating myself and letting myself fester.

Nowadays I make a real effort with this: to remember not to put any more nails in the wall. The people you wrong may forgive you – it's surprising how often they do – but they won't forget you behaved like that, and you have to live with it, too.

Through many of those middle years I employed farm hands Ken and Kathy Gregory. They were full of energy and full of support. After

I thought my problem was drought, end of story. It wasn't. Until I fixed my thinking I was never going to fix any problems.

they left we employed Gerald and Dinah Cox, who also made a huge contribution to us and to Bonavaree. But with the drought biting, I advised Gerald that he was best to seek employment somewhere else if he could.

When you say something like that to a top man he'll just think, *Far out, I'm out of here*, and so he was.

From then on, it was free-fall, the downward journey . . . not that I knew it at the time. For the first few weeks a bit of pressure came off and I thought, *Great, I don't have to pay wages any more.* There was suddenly a big lifeline in the budget, but there was no explanation of how I was going to do all the work that needed to be done.

We dropped a whole new level. Jobs weren't getting done, so I tried to go harder. For the first time in my life Wendy and I were basically farming on our own. She didn't enjoy the physical work at all but we had no choice. It was the only way I could see to survive.

Many years later I spoke to a Canterbury farmer who was fighting drought by employing more people so that everyone could work a bit less. Sure, he had the money to make that choice, but what a resilient response! Imagine if I'd had that wisdom, I thought. I took the other road and took more on myself. The bank never threatened to foreclose on me, and with hindsight I would never have treated myself so hard; but that was the only path that seemed open to me. It was the wrong way. It was a bad, bad decision.

Some time after Gerald left, a car pulled up. Out got this big beaming face that said, 'G'day, Doug, how you going?' It was an old guy, Tom Mason, who in earlier days had been our transport operator in Ward. He was back in the area after years away and he'd heard our farm-hand cottage was empty. 'I'd love to rent it,' he said. He moved in with his wife Myrna and his old Labrador. He was seventy-five and not much use around the farm, but I gave him a four-wheel motorbike and said, 'Just drive around the place. If you see water spewing out, fix the pipe. If you see a broken wire, fix the fence.' By this stage, with me being on my own, the whole place was starting to fall to bits.

Tom was great for me. It was hard to be unhappy when he was around. He'd come whistling down to the yards in the morning when I was feeling absolutely bloody burnt-out. 'Oh, thank God for global warming,' he'd say. 'Imagine how cold it would be today if it wasn't for that!'

He was always trying to entertain me. He stuck a big sign up by our cattle stop: *Kangaroos next 14 kilometres*. And another by the side of the cattle-ramp catwalk: *Slippery when drunk*.

It helped. I find it really hard to work with people that haven't got a sense of humour; after all, we're only on this earth for a short time, and even the most serious stuff has a funny side. And now and again he'd say to me, 'You know what they do with dogs that worry, Doug.' He knew exactly where I was.

Relationships, relationships, relationships: that's what gets me through.

After Fraser came home in 2002, Tom went back to Australia with his wife, but one night a few years later the phone went and it was him. 'Got a bit of a bloody shock the other day,' he said. 'Went to see the doc and I'm buggered. I've run out of runway, Doug.'

He was ringing to ask if he could have his ashes spread up at the top of the farm. 'I want to be able to watch down and make sure you're not slacking.'

So we had a party for him up there at the top of the farm, everyone heading there on four-wheelers and trucks and God knows what. A friend of Tom's started playing the piano accordion and then Myrna opened the ashes container and threw his ashes into the air. A gust of wind caught them and took them out and away, and I suddenly had a realisation that that's the way I want to go. That's what's going to happen with me in the same place.

Blood, sweat and tears – my family's spilt all that on this land. It's part of us, and we're part of it. I never stopped feeling that way, but my big problem in those hard years was that I didn't stop to consider the nature of this place. I was working against it, uselessly trying to make it fit my old ideas about what would work; and in doing so, I was working against myself.

So there I was, clinging fast to my tree trunk, doing what I knew, with no clue how to change the situation, short of praying to God to make it rain. And that went on for years.

I was working like a slave, Canute holding back the waves, and our farm was still probably the best-run farm in the district. But in my eyes it was all rubbish. I knew it was out of control, and that sooner or later my efforts, my sheer physical labour, would not be enough.

Then a godsend. Someone offered us $2.5 million to take the farm off our hands. They brought me a signed purchase agreement. I thought my dream had been answered. 'I'm getting out of here,' I told Wendy. She was appalled. 'If you want to go and look for somewhere else, you go and look, but I'm not coming.' She pointed out it would kill my parents, given they'd poured their lives into the farm. And my grandparents' ashes were buried here. But all I wanted was out of this godforsaken place.

'There's one proviso,' I said. 'I need to find something I'm happy with.'

So I went and looked – further south, then around Australia. I was stunned by the beautiful land stretching out around Toowoomba. When I thought about moving, my heart beat around a thousand miles an hour. But in the end – and Wendy knew this all along – I couldn't do it. The reality of it, and the cost of shifting. And it was lucky because I wanted to run but if I had I would still be running now. All the places I looked at have since had similar problems of drought. So I came home and ripped up that agreement and carried on battling.

If I had run, I would never have stopped running because I would not have addressed my core problems. Core problems? I had plenty of them, but I didn't yet understand what they were. I thought my problem was drought, end of story. It wasn't. Until I fixed my thinking I was never going to fix any problems.

My anger through that time was palpable, and so was my anxiety. But at the same time as I was getting angry and pushing everyone away, I somehow resented the fact that our struggle was so invisible. At one stage during the drought, the Salvation Army came around and delivered food parcels to all the families – that's how bad it was. But they didn't bring any to us; they must have looked at our house and thought we were doing just fine.

They dropped a parcel at our farm cottage, though, where our old farmworker Fred Jones still lived, even though he'd long since retired. He was dying in the hospice at the time, and when I went over to check on the cottage I saw the package and I thought, bugger it, I'm taking that home. I thought, isn't that interesting? People don't realise that these pressures affect everybody. Just because we're supposedly rich in the area doesn't mean that we're coasting this too well. People look at the surface of things.

Nobody knew. A few years later, after JK began to do his depression awareness work, someone might have said, 'Do you actually think Doug's okay?' But people just thought . . . well, I don't know what they thought. But I guess they thought, oh, it's his private business, we won't pry.

13

WHAT DID I MISS?

This year thousands of men will die from stubbornness.

When we look in from the outside, we think other people are doing fine. We don't see their struggles, although we're hyper-aware of our own difficulties. That can lead to us feeling really useless.

We're all losers at something and we're all winners at something. But you only lose if you don't learn. You either win or you learn.

I was asked to chair a breakfast meeting held in our district; we invited three local guys along to share their stories, and I interviewed them about their lives and their achievements, their high points. Then I said, 'Now, would you like to tell us about any of the times when things weren't quite so flash?'

They all got up and shared their stories. These guys were all pillars of the community, very respected. One of them 'fessed up to having had a breakdown; another spoke about how during the drought he'd had no money and was desperate; the third had really struggled during the drought as well. The younger guys in the audience loved it. Hell, they thought, I didn't realise those fellas had all been through this sort of life as well.

Encouraging peers to soften and share stories honestly will do a lot of good for our young. Thankfully there's a huge amount of work being done in this space now and there's a lot of freeing up. It's better for the men and, like I say to groups of men, I've yet to meet a woman who's gutted that her husband has got a little bit more emotional about his life. In fact, the complete opposite is true.

I've met so many women who have paid the ultimate price for their husband's silence.

'My husband committed suicide three weeks ago,' a woman told me after one of my events. 'I never saw it coming.'

Their business, a dairy farm, was flourishing – in fact, just days before her husband died, she had allowed herself to feel their years of struggle were behind them.

'Every Wednesday I'd meet my girlfriends in town. We have lunch together and get our hair done and I get my groceries and come home.' She said, 'I came home and I pushed the button on the door and the door went up and there was his body.'

It's natural to ask, 'What did I miss?' 'Is there something I could have done?' But many people who commit suicide do it without letting on they are thinking about it. This woman had no inkling, and this left her angry.

When I travel around New Zealand I meet a lot of people who have lost someone to suicide. They all want to talk about it, and that's okay – but I want to be involved before that. I want to open up this conversation so that people, especially men, can talk about what's going on inside them.

One guy who spoke to me had been about to kill himself. He went behind the barn out of sight, carrying his gun. And there he saw a Hereford steer had caught its head in the railing. He later said, 'I'll never, ever understand to this day why, but I thought, *I can't do this until I've cleared that up*. I put the gun down and went and got a hammer and I knocked the rail off and the steer ran off down the paddock. As it went down the paddock I thought, *I'm some use*.' It was such a tiny thing, but that flash of good feeling rescued him.

'That's how close I was,' he told me.

'Thank God you didn't do it,' I said.

At my talks I always say: 'Three times as many men commit suicide as women.' I ask the ladies in the room: 'Why do you think that is?' They instantly respond: 'Because men don't talk.' I've asked that question at every presentation, and I have never had to tease out the answer.

Then one day a guy at the back of the room hopped up and said, 'The women talk and they talk and they talk and that's why us men commit suicide.' The whole room, men and women, burst out laughing. From that time on I always brought that up, and it softened the whole argument. Some people think, oh, gee, that's a bit bloody rough – but no, it's not. The moment you soften things with humour, you get your message through. Hard is concrete – there's no penetration. Soft is the way.

I was a classic case. I didn't want to talk to anyone.

I got into computers very early and, while I was in my bad place, my computer was one of the tools I used to isolate myself. I shut myself in my office and played games. Kids' games. *Olympic Decathlon*. It was the only place I could be happy because while I was playing virtual sports or shooting aliens, I could forget about the farm. I never let stock suffer, but playing those games was the only thing that didn't make me feel worse.

Wendy used to scream at me sometimes. 'Get out of the house, I can't bear you in here. Go out and do something. What are you doing? You're just playing again.'

That only made me angry about her. I used to have these thoughts: *Maybe if I was on my own, maybe all this trouble and this yelling and stuff would stop.*

I just wanted the world to go away and leave me alone.

One of the first things that people do as they fall into depression is they isolate themselves. A depressed person is an isolated person. A person whose business isn't going well, the last thing they want to do is tell other people about it. I understand that. It's a pride thing. Pride is a highly valued prize in anyone's life and I think in men it's especially high. When your business is going wrong, your pride, your identity is up for challenge.

Rural people in particular are used to being self-sufficient. They can lead isolated lives, and find it hard to ask for help.

I was the same. I denied that I had a problem. I was aware that things weren't going right, but I felt it was everything else that was wrong, not me.

Despite how hard it is, the starting point is to share with somebody else. We have the language now, and it's so important to be using it. Some guys even say, 'I've got a touch of the JKs'. And everyone – the doctor, their mates, their family – knows just what is meant. Or they might say, 'I'm a bit depressed – it's an illness, not a weakness.' But if you can't ask for or accept help, you've really got trouble.

Isolation is both a symptom and a driver of depression.

Anyone who knows me will tell you that I talk all the time. Communication is such a huge part of my life. I love to talk to the people I'm with, family or friends, and, as Wendy says, if the phone goes, I rush to it, hardly able to wait to talk to whoever it is.

When I was fifteen and home for school holidays, a neighbour

Rural people in particular are used to being self-sufficient. They can lead isolated lives, and find it hard to ask for help.

rang me up. 'We've got a debate in Kaikoura next week and we're one speaker short. Come around to my house tomorrow night and we'll tune you up and you'll be the third speaker.'

That was the first time I'd ever debated. I won top speaker that night. *Damn*, I thought, *I love that!* So when I left school, I joined the Flaxbourne Young Farmers Club. We had two debating teams and we were the best in the top of the South Island.

At eighteen I entered Young Farmer of the Year and I won Marlborough and came fifth in the Tasman final. I quite enjoyed that and so I thought I'd have another go. I won Marlborough again the next year and came fourth in Tasman. I was up against twenty-nine-year-olds and there's a hell of a difference between a nineteen-year-old and a twenty-nine-year-old. But then I fell in love and started all that sort of stuff and didn't ever enter again.

The reason I won was that I could communicate to people. I could stand on my feet and just let people know where we were going and take control. I loved that.

In my talks now, I always tell people that I went quiet for years. They don't really believe me, and I admit it's hard to imagine, but during that horrible time I did. I lost the art of communicating.

To me, if anybody loses that ability to communicate, there is a problem. In fact, that's what I see as the main telltale sign that something is wrong.

One night not long ago, the phone went at half past nine and it was a guy I'd never met – a dairy farm manager who'd looked me up after reading something about me in one of the farming magazines. 'I just wondered if I could have a bit of a talk to you,' he said.

'Yeah, that's no problem at all,' I told him. I could immediately pick the urgency.

'I just can't carry on any more,' he said.

I asked him to tell me about himself. 'I'm managing a farm for a guy, and I've got a little block of my own. My wife and I do all the milking. In the wintertime I plant trees on the home block and I take all the cows over there and I feed them on crops.'

He hadn't had a holiday in five years. He'd just worked himself to a standstill. When he finally slowed up a bit I asked him: 'Does your wife know anything about this?'

'No,' he said, 'I wouldn't tell her.'

'Why not?'

'She wouldn't want to hear this stuff.'

'She probably does,' I said. 'How are you going for mates?'

'I've exploded at pretty much everybody.'

'Yeah, I've done that,' I told him. 'What about stock agents and stuff?'

'I told them all to piss off.'

'I want to ask you to do something for me,' I said. 'When you get off this call I want you to tell your wife. Just say, "Honey, sit down, I've got to tell you something." I want you to tell her what you've just told me. She won't react the way you think she's going to react. She will have been waiting for you to tell her what's wrong. She will have picked that it's not right. She'll be just dying for you to share with her. Then you've both got to do something that's going to be the hardest thing you've ever done: write out a list of the people that you need back in your life and ring them up one by one and ask them if they can come around and have a cup of tea.'

I could hear his ragged breathing.

'When you've done that,' I told him, 'you'll feel so good that you'll wonder why this phone call ever happened. I'm going to ring you in a week and see how far you've got.'

A little later, I rang him back, and already he sounded a bit less tense. 'Doug,' he said, 'she was completely different. I didn't realise she'd be sympathetic.'

'All these women are just screaming with pain,' I told him. 'Like my wife, she was just like, *Why have you left me?* I'd left my wife but I was still living here.'

We all have dreams, but when the dream is lying in ruins, and all you have is endless work, and kids to worry about, and a wife you don't think will understand – nobody can handle these pressures alone.

Everybody is the same. The unlucky ones end up with a funeral on their hands, and I've met far too many people in that situation: where they come home to a suicide and their loved one had never let on how bad things were getting.

So the starting point has to be here, at the most basic point: to communicate.

I know it's scary, but the benefits are huge and, often, immediate. When we hide ourselves away and refuse to engage with the world, and don't share our feelings and despair with the people close to us, we are, in effect, running away. And the less we talk, and the faster we run, the bigger and more intractable those problems become.

So the key part to my story, really, is that I progressively realised I had to win by not running. I had to solve my problems, and a big part of facing up to them was sharing them. I'll say it again: none of us can do this thing called life all alone.

And if you're the one watching someone you love sink into depression, don't be afraid to seek help – for them, for yourself. One couple who approached me after an event were very worried about their son. They farmed in a remote rural valley, and he now lived on the other side of the valley with his wife and kids. He had been an active family man, captain of his rugby team and so on, but in the last couple of years he'd changed. He'd become aggressive – they could hear his voice from across the valley, yelling at his family. They'd taken a fair bit of abuse from him themselves. They knew something was wrong, but they'd become afraid. 'What can we do?' they asked.

I said to them, 'Basically what you're saying to me is you can no longer communicate with your son?'

'It just always ends up in yelling,' they agreed.

'Has he still got any friends?'

'He's chased most people away. There's one guy that he still has a little bit to do with.'

'He's your only hope. Go and have a talk to him, and see if he can suggest to your son that he's changed.'

I believe it is possible to help people. Nearly all those people who are struggling so badly are screaming for help – it's just they don't know how to ask.

14

WENDY'S STORY

Partners go through hell when the person they love is sunk in depression. The greatest need for support is probably among those coping with people like me. Sad, but true. Wendy has since shared her experience of that time. In 2015 she was the guest speaker at an event put on by Farming Women Tairawhiti, a group of farming women who have organised themselves for mutual support. Wendy now says that her first piece of advice for someone living with a person with depression is: tell someone and get support. This is her story of that time.

Doug slipped into depression gradually. It didn't happen overnight.

I saw him isolating himself more and more. Normally, he loves yarning on the phone; if the phone rings, he always runs to get it. It doesn't matter who it is because he loves chatting so much. Progressively that stopped and he wouldn't go near the phone. And I thought, *If he's not going to answer it, I'm not going to answer it.* There would be messages on the phone: 'Doug, can you ring . . .' and I'd say to him, 'You've got to ring so-and-so,' and he wouldn't ring them and they'd ring back and I'd say, 'He's not here.' I never told anybody. Not a soul. I lied to people: I just kept saying, 'He's not here, he's not here,' or 'He's sick. He's in bed.' I never said, 'Help me.' Not even to my sisters, or my friends.

Meanwhile, it got drier and drier and drier. A few times it teased us – we'd see clouds crossing the horizon – and he'd go outside and just scream ghastly language looking up above.

He'd get very angry, sometimes with me. It was scary – he'd throw things. I always knew it was fuelled by alcohol, that he was drinking a lot. I tried tipping alcohol out. I don't know how much I tipped down the sink, but of course I didn't achieve anything because he just went out and bought more. How he didn't have a road accident I don't know. He'd be that drunk and he'd go off and buy more. But his drinking was always in the security of his little den.

I tried having dinner earlier because I thought he was less likely to drink after dinner. That worked sometimes. I did tell a few friends that he was drinking, but I never told them the full story. I just could never say to anybody, 'Look, can you help Doug? He's in a mess.'

I feared he would take his own life. Sometimes he would pack a bag and take off. I'd be like an old detective, looking to see if he'd taken anything he could hurt himself with. But I think he just drove. Drove and drove.

We were hardly even speaking to each other.

Isolation is definitely an issue for rural people, but maybe it's the same no matter where you live. Doug was in his office, drinking and playing games on the computer, and just hating every minute of life; I was also hiding in our house and not reaching out to anyone. One of the reasons was shame. I felt that I had failed, and he felt he'd failed. I didn't want to be a total failure by having a marriage that had absolutely collapsed. I hung in there.

I often rang Alcoholics Anonymous and Lifeline, especially when he'd gone into a fury, and that was my comfort, talking to somebody. But the bottom line was they needed to see us to be able to help us and I couldn't get Doug to seek help. He totally rejected any help; he didn't even think he had a problem. He thought it was everybody else who had let him down, and I was included in that: he blamed me, too, for the way things had gone so horribly wrong.

We would get invites to go out socially and he'd say, 'I'm not going.' Or sometimes we would get halfway there but he couldn't do it. I remember once we were heading to a party and he stopped the car and I said, 'Where are you going?' He said, 'I'm going home.' He walked all the way over the hills home. I don't know what he said to the babysitter but she was still here in the morning.

On that occasion I carried on and told people he wasn't well. But nobody said, 'We never see him.' I think a lot of people probably sort of knew and steered clear of him.

Why did I stay? One reason was that we still had a child at home. Doug could just take off; I couldn't. Also, I remained really fearful that he was going to take his own life, and I couldn't have lived with myself if I left him and that happened. He tried his best to get rid of me: he told me many times, 'Get out. I don't want you here. Just get out.' But I thought, *No way, I'm not going.*

And I remembered that I loved him, and I quietly thought he would come back. But it was hard. It was the lack of communication that was so hard: I was in a silent world, really, because he just didn't talk at all.

When I went on the Resilient Farmer road trip with Doug in 2015, lots of women wanted to talk to me. So many were in the same situation, and that was what they all said to me: my husband's pushing me out.

Now these things are more openly talked about. When Doug and I were going through those years, there weren't the words or the social pathways for speaking of these situations. That has changed and there's more understanding now. And of course Google can find all sorts of amazing things to help you. That didn't exist then.

When my kids ask me what I want for my birthday or whatever, I always say, I just want everybody to be happy. Happy and healthy. It's almost a joke in our family that I always say that. But since that time, when I ask them what they want, they say, 'Mum, look after yourself; please look after yourself.' Because I see now that I wasn't looking after myself. I stopped doing things I enjoyed, and I isolated myself from support.

The one thing I did do was to garden. In those days we didn't have to pay for water we used, so I poured water on the grounds around the house, trying to keep it like a green oasis so that at least we had something to keep us sane. It kept me sane anyway, pouring the water on. Part of our trouble was that we lived at our place of work. Every minute of the day we were confronted with what was going wrong. We never got away from it.

And then he met Derrick Moot. The stock agent who got him to go to that meeting was brave, being persistent with Doug, who was such an angry man at that time. And I remember Doug coming home and saying he hated the trip, he feared for his life, the agent drove too fast, and things like that. But he also said, 'Moot talks sense.' Then he said, 'I'm going to do it. I reckon we can do it.'

It wasn't an overnight transformation. It was a gradual process, but I could see it coming together. I could see there was a light on.

15

THE DICE OF LIFE

If you always do what you've always done you'll always get what you've always had.

The dice of life are not like playing dice with the numbers one to six. The dice of life have risk on every face. When I was in my terrible time I looked in vain for the face that showed no risk, and I can tell you: it doesn't exist. From the moment we're born to the day we die, we face risk. Reward lies in finding opportunities to mitigate risk. It took me a long time to realise that, by doing nothing and not changing, I was actually heightening my risk. Clinging to my tree trunk felt safe, but actually it was a terrible place that would have killed me.

I remember a conversation I had with my father many years ago. He had just come across the idea that, in the future, the average person will have to retrain several times in their life. This is widely talked about now, but it was a new idea at the time. *Poor everyone*, I thought. What I failed to realise was that everything in my own life was screaming at me to change.

Now I feel sorry for the people who think that they don't need to change.

As the drought ground on, and I shut myself away, keeping no company but my own miserable self, I may as well have been signing my own execution order. What happens to a plant if you shut it in the dark? It withers and dies. Growth – life itself – requires sunlight.

What I've come to discover about myself is that fresh ideas, the company of others and opportunities to be inspired are like sunlight falling on me. Give me a fresh idea and I'm like fodder beet. Fodder beet has enormous leaves, like solar panels that turn to the sun to collect the light. But now my life was closing up. I folded up my leaves and became unreceptive to the energy of the world.

Now I know that if it hadn't been the drought it would have been something else. I was skating on such a thin layer of self-knowledge that anything could have sent me crashing through. I was in very dangerous territory.

There are three age groups where suicide rates peak. The first is the eighteen to twenty-four-year-olds, who are learning to manage their own lives and developing their capacity for relationships with other people.

The third group is those aged eighty-five and over. But the second group in which suicide rates spike, especially among men, is between forty-two and fifty-two. That's precisely the age at which I was doing it hardest.

It's not hard to see why. In their thirties, most people are establishing career paths, having children, consolidating their own home – it's such an exciting time, filled with promise. That was certainly the case for Wendy and me: we were busy and happy and we thought life would always be filled with forward movement.

But then, in their forties, a lot of people look around and what they see isn't nearly as good as they thought it was going to be. Visions aren't being realised. Goals are more difficult to achieve, or they slip like water through the cracks of everyday life.

As for me, I stagnated, and this reinforced my negative feelings about where I'd got to in life. I didn't know it, didn't have the language for it, but my learning curve had reduced. I didn't understand the equation between continuous learning and continuous excitement. I needed to jump forward, but I was too busy blaming the external circumstances of the drought to realise my future was in my own hands.

And then a miracle happened. The phone went one day and it was a young stock agent called John Ladley.

'G'day, Doug, I'm just ringing to see if you're interested in going to a field day in North Canterbury next week.'

'What's it on?'

'It's on lucerne.'

'Who's speaking?'

'A fellow called Derrick Moot. A lecturer at Lincoln University.'

'What would he tell me about lucerne? Our family's been growing it for eighty years.'

'It'll do you good to get off the farm.'

'No, I've got too much on.'

Then there was a pause; he must have grabbed his breath. 'Doug,' he said, 'you haven't got anything on. I'm going to pick you up at six-thirty on Tuesday.'

It was brave of him. I thought, you cheeky little bugger, but I gave up. Sometimes it's easier to do things than not do them. 'Oh, all right.'

So he picked me up and we went down to collect a neighbour

who was also coming along. He'd slept in and we were a quarter of an hour mucking around there while he tore around pulling his pants on, shoving a bit of breakfast into his face. And all the time I was thinking, *I can't be bothered with this. I'll just hop out and head home . . .* I came that close; but part of me was also resigned to getting through the day, already looking forward to getting home that night and shutting myself in my office again.

By that stage we were running late and we had to really motor. We flew down the highway and I was hanging onto the seat, grumbling away to myself. *What a stupid idea this is. I should be at home.* But if I'd been at home I would have been locked in my office doing nothing, probably.

The event was held at Pegasus Bay Winery at Waipara in North Canterbury, and the place was packed with around 200 people, standing room only. I looked around and found I knew nobody but the people I'd come with, so I sat down and prepared to be bored.

Then Derrick Moot took the stage and everyone quietened down. Derrick's a fairly quiet-spoken guy, a plant scientist rather than a farmer, but what he had to say had me sitting up as if I was electrified. Within minutes I was asking someone if I could borrow a pencil, and I began scribbling notes as fast as I could. I thought I knew everything about lucerne, but here I was seeing a whole new picture: Moot introduced me to a plant that would help me better utilise the little water that fell on my paddocks, and which could potentially enormously increase my productivity.

One day, one hour, one man. This guy Moot was offering me new knowledge and a way to generate more feed, if I was prepared to change the way I produced feed crops.

Up until I heard him, I had only two solutions to my problems, and they were to cut costs and work harder. Those are both zero-sum games. You quickly get to a point where there are simply not enough hours in the week. It's a very unsustainable strategic position to be in. Moot was suggesting something else. All it required was a radical departure from my norm. It was hope, albeit dressed up in a lot of uncertainty.

After the meeting I was desperate to get home. The others wanted to stop and have dinner, so it was late by the time we returned. Wendy had gone to bed, but I went straight to my computer and brought up all my spreadsheets and thought, *How can I do this?* I knew what it cost to establish a paddock.

At about half past three in the morning Wendy came out and said, 'What the hell are you doing?'

'I'm building us a new dream,' I said. 'We're going to have another crack.'

I don't know whether she was impressed or not, but for me the light had gone on.

PART THREE

16

A BUCKET UNDER THE PADDOCK

Dr Derrick Moot is now a professor in plant science at Lincoln University. But when I first came across him, at the field day in Waipara in 1998, he was setting out in his academic career. He'd recently returned from the UK where he'd worked with the plant scientist J. R. Porter, studying what effects climate change might have on European crops such as wheat. Back then, that was still a fairly radical framework. Moot spent quite a bit of time researching climate change to decide for himself whether he thought it was really happening. He concluded it was. So when he arrived back in New Zealand, he asked himself which local farmers were most vulnerable. His answer: east coast dryland farmers. Those farmers, who of course included myself, were already dealing with real climate challenges.

So he started down a path of trying to foster resilience in dryland farmers.

To Moot, farmer resilience means the ability to cope with the best year and the worst year that the weather may throw at us; it means that we can farm profitably in the medium term, and that we are improving the land, rather than degrading it. He knew that unless a farm was financially viable, farmers could not be expected to fence off waterways or plant riparian strips. He saw the whole picture: sheep and beef farmers on the east coast of New Zealand were financially very vulnerable, and therefore their communities were also socially vulnerable, and those conditions can lead to environmental vulnerability because, in financial stress, people will overgraze and make poor decisions about land management.

Dryland farmers needed help, and he thought, 'If I don't do it, who will?' No one else was doing research in this area.

MAF's Farm Advisory Service – which used to provide independent advice to farmers – was disbanded in the 1980s when the country adopted a new economic paradigm where the market, rather than the government, was believed to provide all the answers. Since then, the dairy industry and the seed and fertiliser companies have dictated most agricultural research.

But Moot looked at our situation and he saw market failure: over time, farmers would not make enough money to be profitable and would eventually go out of business. Yes! That was exactly what was happening to me in 1998.

Moot, though, working inside a university, could determine his own research direction. He set about trying to understand what our problems were, and he saw that while we largely grew traditional pastures of ryegrass and white clover, these species were not suited to our particular conditions.

Ryegrass and clover are classic dairy farm pastures, promoted by seed companies as suitable for everywhere. Yet in the dryland areas, Moot quickly saw we were on a downward spiral: every two or three years those pastures died, unable to withstand the dryness, and had to be resown. For farmers it was a costly loss, but there was no independent advice on what a better system might be.

If you ask drought-stricken farmers what they need, they'll tell you: 'Water . . . if I only had water.' Irrigation thus becomes an obvious, intuitive answer to the problems of dryland farming.

Moot did a couple of simple experiments, and he found that if he poured water alone onto a pasture, the response was negligible. Production of what we call dry matter – that is, the nutritional content of a fodder crop – would only increase from about six tonnes to ten tonnes per hectare, per year: not enough to give a good return on the high cost of converting to an irrigation system.

If he took that same pasture and added nitrogen, and no water, he'd go from six tonnes to fifteen tonnes. If he added both water and nitrogen – which is essentially what dairy systems do – then dry-matter production rose again to twenty-two tonnes.

But as we know, there are high financial and environmental problems with this model.

Moot's attention settled on lucerne, a species of plant that, like many legumes, fixes its own nitrogen from the air.

Lucerne has an incredibly long tap root – I've personally dug up plants whose roots were five metres long – so it's built to maximise whatever moisture is in the ground. In fact, for dryland farmers such as me, lucerne is more than twice as efficient at turning every millimetre of water into nutrition than the pastures on which we were currently grazing our animals. A lucerne tap root is like a great big bucket under the surface of the paddock.

While our traditional pastures of ryegrass and clover wither and die in the furnace of our summers, lucerne thrives in the heat. A single crop of lucerne can grow for more than ten years before needing to be resown.

Moot found that, with lucerne, he could double production of dry matter without adding water or nitrogen, and therefore without adding much cost at all to farmers' systems. You've got to plant something, anyway, he reasoned.

'Lucerne is the most drought-tolerant plant we have,' he concluded. 'Why aren't farmers using it?' And he set out on what's been a twenty-year quest to tell us about it.

In 1998, when I was dragged reluctantly along to hear this young plant scientist talking, I was as ready to hear his message as my drought-ravaged pastures were desperate for rain. Moot, of course, was an idealist back then. He thought if he could come up with a solution – lucerne! – farmers would see the sense, grab it and everything would be hunky-dory. As he came to realise, there are many reasons why that hasn't happened. But unbeknownst to him, there was one farmer in the audience who heard the message and was determined to try it. I was at rock bottom, with no option but to try.

A few years earlier, after I'd sold a whole lot of sheep and had $35,000 rattling around in my pocket, I decided I was going to spend the money on something stupid. I saw a trailer yacht I liked the look of and went down to Lyttelton to have a look at it. It was the best Noelex 25 in the country, a wonderful yacht called *Force Four*. I took it for a spin and I wrote out a cheque for $35,000. *There we are,* I said to myself, and I hooked it on the back of the truck and towed it home.

I started racing the yacht and I would go three times a week down the Marlborough Sounds. The days spent battling the fickle winds of Queen Charlotte generated saving moments of happiness, but also generated another problem: I looked forward to that so much it made me hate the stupid farm even more. All in all, it was the dumbest money I spent.

Now, excited after hearing Moot, I thought, the first thing I've got to do is sell the yacht. A young woman had previously approached me to ask if she could buy *Force Four*, so I rang her and we completed the deal in a day. I got my $35,000 back and I poured every cent of that back into the farm, converting my paddocks to lucerne.

I did a business deal with myself. For every year the company had that $35,000 I would pay myself the interest rate of one metre of yacht per year, and eventually I'd be able to buy myself a new one. Sure enough, a few years later I bought *Blue Velvet*, a beautiful eleven-metre yacht. I tell myself that if I only spend one day a month on the boat, how valuable is that day if it stops me from going mad?

That night, looking at my spreadsheets, full of hope after hearing Derrick Moot tell me I could do things differently, I at last realised I was at a crossroads. It was as though there was a big sign saying *The rest of my life.* There were two paths, one labelled *Average* and the other *Memorable*, and both were full of risk and danger. There was no guarantee that *Memorable* would be successful; but to my fevered brain, activated by the hope I'd just been handed, it seemed a better punt. Risk. I was about to have another throw at the dice of life.

17

THE CHANGE CYCLE

The process of change is so bloody hard because it's usually not initiated until too late. Most people will only change once they've been convinced that things are quite seriously wrong, by which stage all the factors that could have eased the process have already been destroyed.

In our early years, Wendy and I had a lot of success. We took over the business, we worked like hell, we bought more farms and the children came.

We were really happy and we thought, life is great – we've got this sorted. Like most people in our Western culture, I thought life was linear – that it would simply progress. I didn't understand that life is not like that. It's actually far more complex, and comes in cycles of growth and decline, change and learning.

So, in those years of success, when everything was screaming at me, *Change. You need to change*, I failed to hear it. Change was the last thing on my mind. Everything was going so well, and I had always been taught not to change what's not broke.

But everything we make will fail if we don't attend to it.

When things went wrong – the drought struck and my farming model failed – it was too late to comfortably instigate change because I was heading downwards, my resources were dwindling and I felt, *I can't change now because everything's going wrong*. Like most people in that situation, I actually went the other way: *I wanted to change less*. That was me: I was clinging to my tree trunk.

When I did begin to change – when I got fired up about lucerne and began replanting our paddocks and tried to feed our stock this new way – things didn't get better. In fact, they got worse.

I poured money into the farm and, year by year, extended our lucerne paddocks from about thirty hectares to around 450 hectares today. I didn't use contractors at all in those days but did all the work myself, following my usual 'just do it' habit. I was a man on a mission, really excited about the prospect of a solution to this terrible problem. From what Moot was saying, I thought I would get a reasonably quick return. Establishment was good and my hopes were high.

But the next winter was really dry and cold and the lucerne shut down, as it always does in winter, and by spring, when the lambs started dropping, there was no lucerne for them to eat. You can't say to the lambs, 'Hold on, go back. We're just not ready for you yet.' I had all these lambs running around the place on mothers that weren't being fully fed, and to top it all off, we experienced metabolic problems with ewes that were not used to the new feed. Initial lamb development was poorer than ever. Instead of going forwards, we went backwards.

I was gutted; but at least I recognised the problem. My neighbours, Chris Pascoe and Jane Mitchel, had grown a crop of Omaka green-

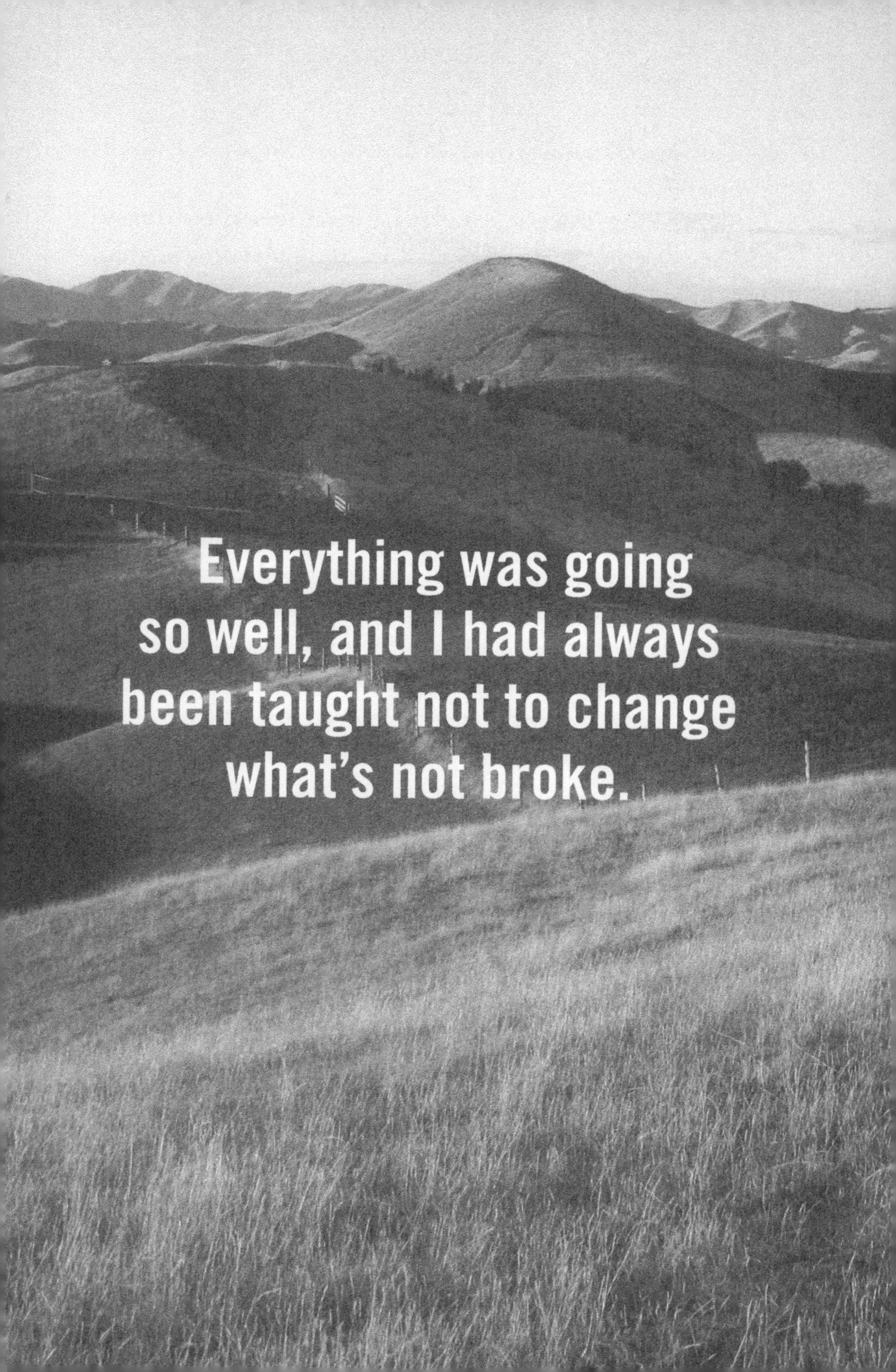

Everything was going
so well, and I had always
been taught not to change
what's not broke.

feed barley, and I realised this held the key to filling the late winter/early spring feed gap.

The next year, results were better, and a warmer winter meant we had more lucerne. That second season we had a bit of rain, which brought on a lush green flush in the lucerne, which in turn gave me a charge of optimism. Feed surpluses were emerging and lamb growth looked amazing.

But one morning I went out into my beautiful spring-green farm, and when I reached the first lucerne paddock it was strewn with white bodies. I rushed around the farm. Dead ewes lay in every paddock.

Those sheep hadn't been able to handle the high-octane, lush legume pasture and had died of bloat. This is a condition where pressure builds in the rumen – the first stomach, which is rather like a large fermentation vat where bacteria and other microbes break down the feed – but the animals can't belch the gas and the resulting pressure can cause heart and lung failure.

I returned to the house in despair. 'I've buggered our future,' I told Wendy.

'I'll come and give you a hand to clean the place up,' she said. By this stage our ewes were huge and lifting them was impossible on my own. Together we buried the dead sheep.

I shared the story with Dad.

'You have to turn back, Doug,' he said. 'You're on the wrong road.'

Were we simply getting ourselves deeper into trouble? I was almost breaking under the strain, but I couldn't do as he said. There was nowhere to turn back to. I knew the road I had been travelling was of little use, and yet I also knew that to give up was certain failure.

My mental health was ridiculous at that time, but because I couldn't let go of this glimmer of hope, this sniff of an opportunity, I kept going. I relate to what John Kirwan says about hope: hang on to it. It's no good telling people to harden up if they have no hope.

But I'd been handed some hope, and it was still empowering me. As long as I still had some hope I could harden up as good as gold. I cracked on.

Of course I had self-doubt – a lot of self-doubt. But when I thought about it objectively I knew that the old way was failing. I'd rather go broke trying than go broke giving up. I was beginning to understand that change entailed a bit of rough stuff – that it required sacrifice from somebody. I'll be that person, I thought.

So in those first two or three years we didn't get the gold rush that I was looking for, but every year our understanding and knowledge increased and we suffered fewer ewe deaths, and it was enough to make me pleased that something was happening.

It was around this time that a local farmer and columnist for a national newspaper labelled me 'the Lucerne Lunatic'. People in the district thought I'd gone crazy, planting lucerne everywhere. But being called the Lucerne Lunatic made me proud; it was an acknowledgement, after all, that I was doing something different.

Now, when I talk to people about my journey and the massive changes we undertook at Bonavaree, I explain the process by talking about the sigmoid curve. Imagine an 'S' lying on its side, slightly stretched out, rather like gentle waves rolling in to the shore. That's the sigmoid curve, the parabola of change. It's a mathematical concept that illustrates the cyclical motion affecting every area of our lives. It's widely used to model the life cycle of businesses. Essentially, it models change, and it helps me to understand why change is necessary, even in very successful businesses.

The sigmoid curve illustrates the three phases within the life cycle of a business: the learning phase, the growth phase, and the decline phase. It shows that, when you first introduce a change, much hard work is called for. Much effort is expended, for little apparent result. You may even feel you are going backwards as you take on new knowledge through trial and error, and change your processes. It's a very difficult phase, as there is no tangible reward. This was the situation I was in when I first rushed home and began planting my paddocks in lucerne.

Next comes the growth phase when the change is bedded in, and the rewards begin to unfold. This is the wonderful time. Eventually, though, that phase will slow and, if no new changes are introduced, decline will set in. Wendy and I were at this stage as we happily coasted along on the success of our early farm expansion, but hadn't put any thought into fundamentally examining our systems. The point at which I finally had to address the need to change was when we had gone over the peak of the curve and were already skidding down the other side.

Once you understand the sigmoid curve, you realise that the time to make change is while you are still in the growth phase, so that the difficulties of introducing new factors – new technologies, new systems – are offset by current success. It thus becomes a continual cycle.

Smart businesses, whether they're urban or rural, see the need for change before they hit the top of the growth curve. Say your company has had three years in a row of record profits. Most people would say that's a sign of absolute success, but I would now say this is a real worry. It's actually a point of challenge. In a top business there is no day where things don't need more attention; otherwise, decline will set in and the curve will inevitably take you downwards. There's no rest area.

And when businesses make that change, it will always take them down the curve before it goes up. I have never met anyone who's had a positive gain immediately after implementing change. New resources must be paid for, people need retraining and support, production might slow. At that point, the business owner might panic. *I've spent fifty grand on this process but we're getting no reward.* So the temptation is to go back – but if you retreat, not only is the change not made, but you lose all the money you invested. There's always an investment – of money, of course, but also of emotional energy – before you earn your reward.

In short, any change will set you back before it takes you forward. If you're not prepared for this, you'll be overwhelmed by doubt and fear, give up and just keep clinging to your tree trunk – which is what Dad advised me to do on that dreadful day when our sheep were dying of bloat.

The loneliest time in my life was when we instigated change, because for a long time we went downwards. I was already down and we went further down. When I embarked on this new process of committing to lucerne, I had not prepared myself for the years when it didn't seem we were making any progress. I wasn't ready for my beautiful sheep dying in the paddocks.

When I talk to people about the sigmoid curve, they can understand it. The theory is good and most people easily see how it applies to someone else. But applying it to yourself is really hard. It feels like high risk and takes a lot of faith that you've made the right decision, because for a while the signs seem to point in the wrong direction. What got me through was courage, and the collaborative support of those people who held my hand through that time that said, 'No, you're doing the right thing but you've just got to keep going now. You can't afford to turn back.'

Gradually our knowledge improved. We learned more about lucerne and its capabilities. Once I began giving public talks about our adaptations I would always be clear about the hard times, but few would listen. They just thought, 'Plant lucerne . . . success.' Consequently, many who followed fell into similar traps, and gave up

Smart businesses, whether they're urban or rural, see the need for change before they hit the top of the growth curve.

in disgust. But others persevered and today the plant is used widely across our land.

I thought I was learning about lucerne; I now know I was learning about change itself, and I've been able to apply that understanding to every aspect of my business. Today when I look at our farm, our stock and our bank account I am so pleased I did not turn back. Those tiny beams of light that reached me all those years ago have turned into rays of sunshine, delivering results way beyond my wildest expectations.

18

A FARMER OF WATER

It's a small world that we live in. Four years after I heard Derrick Moot speak in Waipara – four years in which I struggled to implement his system – our paths crossed again in the most unexpected way.

I was in Blenheim one day, browsing in the supermarket, when I spotted a woman who had been a teacher when my kids were at school. We chatted for a few minutes, and I asked after her daughter. 'She married a guy called Derrick Moot,' she told me.

I was stunned. 'He saved my life,' I told her.

Not long after that, I got a phone call. 'You won't know me,' a man's voice said, 'but I'm Derrick Moot. I'm staying with my mother-in-law in the Sounds and I'd like to come out to your farm.' He told me later he was nervous – he'd never cold-called a farmer before. His mother-in-law had told him about our meeting in the supermarket, and when it got to the part where I said that Moot had saved my life, he was gobsmacked. These days, rural people say things like that to him all the time, but back then it had never happened before. They told him I was known as the Lucerne Lunatic. He was excited, although apprehensive: here was a farmer who had taken his principles and put them into practice. He wanted to come and see for himself.

I couldn't believe my ears. I'd heard Moot tell his audience that lucerne was 'God's plant' – well, as far as I was concerned, Moot himself was God. God was on the phone!

'I've spent the last four years trying to put your bloody system in place,' I told him, 'and it's just about killed me. Having you here on the farm would be the same as inviting the Queen to come and visit us. If you want to come here the door is always open.'

He did come over, and we hopped in my truck and I showed him what I'd done. The lucerne was an emerald contrast with the summer-dry hills. Between the dark days of never-ending new problems, we had begun to see light. I was able to tell him I was already getting a better result, thanks to the high nutrition content of the lucerne. Lambs fed by lucerne-eating mothers were so healthy and big they could go straight off their mother to the processor – these are high-profit lambs as they have virtually no extra costs attached. And lambs grown on lucerne had a higher meat content than those grown on traditional feed, so each carcass earned more money.

I felt it was pathetically little to show. I didn't yet realise that most major change is slow. Major change takes time and long-term commitment – and that's why most people don't like change and most fail.

And then came the insight that completely turned me around. I was talking about the problems of rainfall variability, and musing about whether I had the right sheep genetics, or the right plants, when he broke in.

'Actually,' he said, 'your job is to farm the water you do get as well as you possibly can.' He looked out at the valley of lucerne, where so much of the value was hidden underground in those giant tap roots that collect water no other plant has access to.

'You are a farmer of water,' he said. And the light went on.

Our old system – the system that was still running me ragged, and leaving me always trying to catch up – was based around trying to finish lambs in the summer, when we don't have water. From early January, the ryegrass – which is sold as 'the permanent pasture' – gave up in the heat and dry, so it was always a struggle to finish the lambs. We'd feed them on cut-and-carry lucerne and hay harvested the previous spring.

With my new lucerne acreage I had been moving away from this old way, but I hadn't had the conceptual underpinning to really understand what I was doing. But when Moot told me I was a farmer of water, everything began to make more sense.

'Once you start thinking about the water, then you start designing your system around when you do have moisture,' he said. 'When your rivers are running, that's water running off your farm. Grass will only hold so much water, but your lucerne crop creates a great big bucket, so that when you get your rainfall, it keeps it. And your rivers don't flow off your farm until you've got full saturation of the soil profile.'

I was so excited to have him there that I talked and talked, and he listened carefully and was able to feed back to me the theory underlying my practice, or to explain something about the plant itself that I hadn't realised.

'I put the lucerne in the ground,' I told him, 'and it grows to about six inches and then it just stops. It seems really slow to grow.'

'That's because it's growing its roots,' he said. 'At the other end of the plant, out of sight in the ground, it's growing at the rate of about one centimetre a day.'

When you see a lucerne root, it's pretty obvious – they are huge and knobbly and reach metres down into the ground. Compare it to a ryegrass root and it's like comparing Jonah Lomu's leg with a baby's finger. A lucerne root looks like the engine it is – a water transfer station and an energy converter that was making a best friend out of my old enemy the sun. Knowing that made me even more enthusiastic. I would have to be patient, although that's not something that comes naturally to me.

Driving around the farm with Moot was another kind of beginning for me. As my situation had declined, as my farm was dying and I isolated myself in my despair, my attitude had hardened. I became like concrete; I repelled everything. But now a big softening was under way – my attitudes were easing and my heart was opening up. I was realising the possibilities of collaboration and sharing, and the potential for learning from others.

You might say we human beings are not so different from the plants we grow. When they turn their leaves to the sun they use their capacity to absorb and deliver energy.

And Moot was as pleased as I was. It was humbling that someone had trusted him enough to put theory into practice, he said. As an academic he had no real way of knowing, when he dropped his stone into the water at talks he gave to rural folk, just what ripples he was causing in the pond. He didn't have any farm experience, so coming to Bonavaree he was able to get a good feeling for how it all worked.

And now here I was with my farm and my problems, my trials and errors – and he could come out of the lab and into the real world. Whenever I presented him with a problem, he knew that if it was a problem for me, there would be a hundred other farmers asking the same question. He really wanted it to work for us, and he was tireless in his support. We both believed that as I was farming in a particularly dry part of the country, if I was successful, there was no reason why it couldn't be successful elsewhere.

'I can guarantee you're growing twice as much feed as you were before,' he said with satisfaction, looking out at my lucerne pastures.

'Yeah,' I replied, 'but when I put these animals on here, some of them are dying.' If it had been up to Dad, we would have stopped our lucerne process right there – and this is exactly the point many other farmers have reached.

Moot explained that the ruminant stomach is a marvellous thing – it's like a city of life in there – but it does need time to adapt. If I move animals from eating grass every day onto lucerne, which is much richer, it takes about ten days for the microbiota in the animal's stomach to adapt to effectively manage that feed.

People don't understand that change takes time. I didn't understand it myself. So when I later began reporting to people that we'd increased our fertility scanning by thirty-five per cent when we mated on lucerne as opposed to grass, some farmers thought: 'Well I've got two lucerne paddocks, next year I'll mate my ewes on that.' They put the ram out and put the sheep onto the lucerne, but what they didn't realise is it takes time for that ewe to adjust to that new feed. Action without knowledge . . . The ewes would get sick, some would die, and that farmer would decide lucerne was rubbish and wouldn't touch it again. What a lost opportunity.

Now, when we introduce animals to 'God's plant', we'll turn them into a paddock that's got grass and lucerne in it. They'll have a bit of lucerne so that the microbiota that work on breaking it down will begin to build up.

Moot helped me understand the scale of the change I was introducing. Switching from ryegrass to lucerne is like going from driving a Mini to trying to control a Ferrari. Lucerne is high-octane and out of control until you know how to handle it.

For instance, animals that are growing very rapidly will consume soil, and in that soil there are clostridial bacteria, which cause tetanus in humans and diseases in animals. Those animals are growing so fast, their immune system can't keep up, and if they haven't been vaccinated they will die quickly. Following that first conversation with Moot, I increased my rate of vaccination.

'What we're talking about here is not incremental change,' he explained. 'It's transformational change. It's big-step change, and that takes a lot of energy.'

Together, over the years, we refined my system. From that time on I would hate to guess how many emails have gone backwards and forwards, how many times he's been here. We've done episodes of *Rural Delivery* and *Country Calendar*, and Moot wrote me a reference for the Landcorp Agriculture Communicator of the Year, which I won in 2013.

We as a family are part of Moot's success story, but, while we're one of the most dramatic examples of farming transformation using lucerne, the sales figures tell the story of wider change also. Lucerne seed is still a tiny part of overall seed sales, but twenty years ago when Moot began his crusade, seed companies sold 20 tonnes of lucerne seed; now they sell 200 tonnes. What a difference one man can make.

19

LEARNING, STRIVING, REWARD

One of my neighbours was a farmer I considered much worse off than me. His land was more scarred, his sheep much thinner than mine – terrible skinny things you could practically pick up with two fingers. I was out working along the boundary one day when I saw this fellow. *Man*, I thought, *he must be feeling awful down with his farm looking like that*.

'How are things going?' I asked.

'Not too bad,' he replied. He looked surprisingly cheerful.

'This is a bad drought,' I said gloomily, waving my arm in the direction of the parched, dusty hillsides and the dead grass.

'Nothing like we used to get back where I come from.'

Heavens, I thought, *you've hardly got anything but dirt left on your farm.*

I stumbled home. I couldn't figure it out. He's happy! How could he be happy? Why was I so sad?

I didn't have the self-knowledge to realise what was happening to me. I thought it was the drought that was driving me to despair, and yet all around me were people experiencing the same weather patterns, but dealing with it differently.

Over those years I saw many people watch their businesses fall to bits around them. What was once fruitful just turned to dust and they seemed to accept it. It made me so angry and bitter because I couldn't understand. Objectively, Bonavaree was still doing better than most other properties, yet I was suffering a greater sense of failure than many of my peers.

How pointless it is to compare ourselves to others. We learn nothing about ourselves when we do that. There is no objective measure of failure or success; no objective equation linking failure and success to our happiness levels. We can only judge ourselves against our own aspirations, expectations and standards. At that time, in that drought-afflicted place, someone else might have been happy to have broken even; all I could see was that there was no profit. If I wasn't going forward, I was going backwards. That set me apart in my experience from friends and neighbours who had quite different aspirations in life.

My experience of despair was something my father never went through in relation to his work as a farmer. He never struggled financially at all. He bought the farm from his parents, paid it off and then simply farmed it till he sold it to Wendy and me. I could have done as he did – yet I always knew that wasn't a viable pathway for me. To just accept my lot, to repeat my father's life, would have meant nothing to me. It was too easy.

I displayed that difference right at the beginning, when I fought to convince Dad to buy Glen Erin and began to expand Bonavaree. At the time, however, I didn't have this overview, this understanding. I never said to myself, *I don't want to repeat my Dad's life; I want a life of learning, striving and reward.* In fact, I admired my father so much and wanted to be like him in many ways.

It was only much later that I saw more clearly how different we were in our aspirations, and because I didn't have that self-awareness, I was stuck. It's the difference between having your nose pressed against something so that your vision is completely obscured, and standing back for a broader view of the scene. I was so damn busy pressed up close and trying to make the old ways work, I never stood back to adjust my perspective.

To this point in my life, physical 'turn up' (the tough, rural-male ethos of sheer bloody grunt) had always solved my problems. Working hard – from rugby, to school, to farming – had always worked for me. Every time I put in the hard yards, I got results; I beat the challenge; I felt I was in control.

When drought came along, I tried to beat it in the same way, looking to the past for my solution. *Come on, Doug, just work harder. Pull the switch back and get into it.* But for the first time, I couldn't; the enduring torture of drought was greater than my ability to respond. I didn't really understand it at the time, but now I see that my whole value system was being dragged underground by a force for which I had no answer.

Developing lucerne was a crucial step: we could answer nature's challenge with a practical new system. But it wasn't going to solve the problem in my own head, which was that I had reached my personal limits. I needed more, but I didn't yet know it.

One day, another door opened. I got a phone call from a farmer I admired, Johnny Peter. 'Doug,' he said in his blunt way, 'the district's buggered. We've got to do something about it.'

He was setting up a meeting, he told me, with the Landcare

Trust to get some talking started about how we could deal with the challenges the weather was chucking at us. Would I come?

Landcare? The NZ Landcare Trust is a non-governmental organisation that helps farmers improve their land management. I didn't know a lot about them, but one thing was certain: I was highly suspicious of any outsiders coming in and telling us how to run our businesses. On the other hand, here was an opportunity to work with Johnny, whom I had long respected. I knew that if I could work with him, I'd learn from him.

'Yes,' I said.

I had no idea that one short phone call was the beginning of a new journey that would transform my thinking and my life.

Clockwise from top left: Bonavaree homestead, built in 1905; the view from the hill behind the house; a family portrait – I'm sitting on Dad's knee; with Wendy on our wedding day, 1976; Mum and Dad harvesting lucerne shortly after the war; my dad, Graham Avery, in his flying gear.

Top: Wendy with our grandchildren, left to right: Quinn, Eddie, Georgia and Oliver.
Bottom: Our kids, left to right: Fraser, Richard and Alice.

Top: Dad, watched by Mum and Fraser, planting his last tree, shortly before he died.
Bottom: Grandson Oliver and me planting native trees.

Top: Darcy Hooper-Smith moving some ewes. **Middle:** Harvesting lucerne seed.
Bottom: The same piece of land, before (left) and two weeks after the summer rain.

Top left: Me in an autumn-sown rape crop. **Top right:** A handful of lucerne.
Bottom: My first Everest – One Tree Hill, Grassmere Valley.

Opposite page, top left: John Peter at Danseys Pass. **Top right:** Derrick Moot, the man bringing science to the farm. **Middle left:** Fraser with Graeme Ogle. **Middle right:** With John Kirwan – the finest 'sir' in the country. **Bottom:** Passing the baton – with Fraser on the farm.

This page, top: Jim Anderton, telling me about the one that got away.
Middle: Then Minister of Agriculture David Carter and Linda Scott, MP for Marlborough, paying a visit to the Starborough Flaxbourne project. **Bottom:** One of my many presentations, this time to Nuffield scholars in our woolshed.

Top: With Wendy, sightseeing in Greece. **Bottom:** My boat, *Blue Velvet*, at the Walkaway Boating Club regatta – yacht racing is one of my passions.

20

MAN OF VISION

Johnny Peter was born to a poor family from Mangamaunu, just north of Kaikoura. When he was very young, back in the 1930s, his parents' farm failed and they were forced to sell. From that day on, he had a huge chip on his shoulder, but he also had a dream – to get back to farming. He left school as soon as he could, got himself a dog and a nibby stick (a piece of manuka that's been shorn up and made nice and tidy as a walking stick) and went mustering. He set about saving for a horse and another dog and mustered all over the place until he got enough money together to buy a farm – with not much money behind him, he always used to say he bought the most rubbish farms and made the best of them. He went on to buy twelve more farms and sell five during his life's journey.

On his deathbed, as I sat with him, I asked him about regrets.

'If I had my life again, Doug,' he replied, 'I would use more of other people's money.'

I was stunned by this response. Of any farmer I knew, he had used more of other people's money than anyone.

I pondered his words often after that, and compared them with Dad's extreme reluctance to borrow money to buy Glen Erin. I knew that in this arena I was closer in nature to Johnny, who was a tireless searcher after opportunity.

About the time I was first home from college, Johnny bought up several farms at Cape Campbell, a beautiful but windswept peninsula protruding into the south-eastern end of Cook Strait. Trees on this landscape live their lives touching their toes, bent permanently by the endless flow of air rushing from Tasman to Pacific, or in reverse, through that blustery strait. Few trees gain much height as they battle to hold what little ground they have achieved. They're a bit like Johnny was, with his squinted eyes and slight stoop and weathered face – worn by his efforts to achieve.

First impressions of Johnny were of a stern, hard man. He seemed to typify the tough rural male – never more so than on the day he rang me to say he was buggered. The doctors had opened him up and found his heart was already badly damaged. 'You must have had a heart attack some other time,' they said.

'Oh yeah,' he told them. 'I remember when I was way out the back mustering. I got this terrible chest pain and I had to sit down for about four hours before I could move.' It never crossed his mind to ask a doctor about it.

But for all his toughness, to those of us who persisted, he soon revealed his warm and intelligent core. He never stopped developing himself.

Initially I admired him because his development programme turned those badly rundown farms into farms of note. I came to understand that what had driven Johnny's tremendous success as a farmer was not so much his sheer back-breaking labour but his commitment to the systems and processes of farming.

For his farms at Cape Campbell, however, water would always be the limiting factor, as it was for our entire district. Though he built huge dams with concrete spillways, the relentless howling wind sucked up every molecule of wet and took it off into the ocean. When drought came, he was quickly forced to sell animals to preserve his land from the trample of hungry feet. 'Always run under, not over' was his great learning. During this terrible time, Johnny was far better-heeled than we were: confident, established and financially secure. He kept his sense of humour – 'Rain is closer today than what it was yesterday,' he'd say – but he knew something had to be done.

He watched me change my system towards lucerne and was interested, but his background was high country and big country, and he was less comfortable with the intensity of the lucerne model. He figured some deeper thinking was required.

It was heroic of him to be going down that path. We all knew that, as farmers, we were involved in stuff that wasn't good. But when you get caught in the current of despair it's extremely hard to change your direction. No one else had the wherewithal to get out of the current and look for a different way of doing things. We were all too ashamed, too busy running away.

So now here Johnny came, stepping into the heart of my life, a man with a plan. Or, if not quite a plan, a suggestion. He had organised a meeting for a few farmers in the district. He'd invited the Landcare Trust to come and meet us. It was Johnny who knew we had to change, and who had the vision to put our feet on the right road. It was Johnny who first told me, 'The sweetest fruits are on the outside branches; picking fruit is a risky game.' With this new idea of his, we were about to let go of the trunk and start venturing out on unfamiliar branches.

The Marlborough Research Centre is on the outskirts of Blenheim, standing between the town and the endless striated vineyards that now dominate our region. I turned up there one afternoon for the first meeting of what was to become the Starborough Flaxbourne Soil Conservation Group (SFSCG), and found myself one of a small group of about five farmers who'd been identified by Johnny Peter as the ones most likely to start a change process. I felt lucky to be one of the chosen ones, but my hackles were up.

To put my feelings on that day in context, it was just around this time that we – the farmers of the drought-stricken Grassmere area – had taken a hammering in the media from the then co-leader of the Green Party, Rod Donald. Donald had weighed in to the long-running debate over establishing a new terminal for the interisland ferry at Clifford Bay, just north of Lake Grassmere. Donald had described the Grassmere area very disparagingly: what a terrible introduction for tourists, he in effect said, arriving at a place where farmers had destroyed the landscape. His words cut deep. He was of course right, but we were not uncaring; just overrun by circumstance. This happens to humans frequently in cities, too.

We didn't need reinforcement of what we knew; we needed help. I had liked Rod Donald and had strong feelings for his cause, but this kick-started my journey into thinking about effective leadership. While pointing out problems is important, creating solutions is where the real power lies; solutions move people towards change.

On that day of the first meeting with Landcare, I had the safety catch off my six-shooter. Smarting from Rod Donald's words, I thought anyone with a Green leaning was almost certain to try to skin us when we were already skinned to the bone. We were already in total community chaos, financial devastation and environmental devastation. We didn't need to be told that things were wrong; we knew it. I was expecting trouble.

What happened could not have been more different. Landcare CEO Don Ross looked around the room at us, no doubt reading plenty into our weathered skin, our tired, suspicious faces, and he simply asked: 'How can we help?'

I sprang to attention. *Far out,* I thought, *that's a good start.* And the safety catch went back on.

'I want you to tell me what you want,' Don Ross said.

'I want a seventy-inch rainfall,' one of us said.

No you don't, I thought. I could immediately see the fault in his thinking. Obviously, we all knew that wishing for rain was never going to create rain, but that kind of thinking, which we'd all been guilty of, simply showed we didn't understand the problem. Heavy rainfall would destroy this country. Our land, historically, is old seabed that's been pushed up by earthquake action – exactly as happened in the Kaikoura quake of 2016. It's soft, dissolvable clay, full of sodium, and it just melts when wet. A lot of the damage on our hillsides occurred as a result of heavy rainfall.

So I could see, right away, that our problem was us, and the way we used this fragile land. We needed to adapt to the dry – but we didn't have a clue how.

The lights went on for me in that meeting, just as they had when I first listened to Derrick Moot, four years previously, talking about lucerne. It wasn't that I suddenly understood everything that was wrong with my way of thinking, or knew at once what I had to do. I was still only at the very beginning of the process of change. But what lit me up, as I watched Don Ross gently probing us, was a new vision, fuelled by hope and the thrill of learning new things. I started to remember the great feelings that had run through my veins when I was a young farmer starting out with the world at my feet: feelings of value and excitement, and the scent of reward.

I'd said 'yes' when Johnny rang and invited me to the meeting.

Now I said 'yes' when Bonavaree was proposed as one of the experimental farms for the SFSCG. I said I would stand outside while they voted. I was so excited. *I would love to have it; yes, I would.*

I realised I kept saying 'yes' to people, and that was bringing me back to myself.

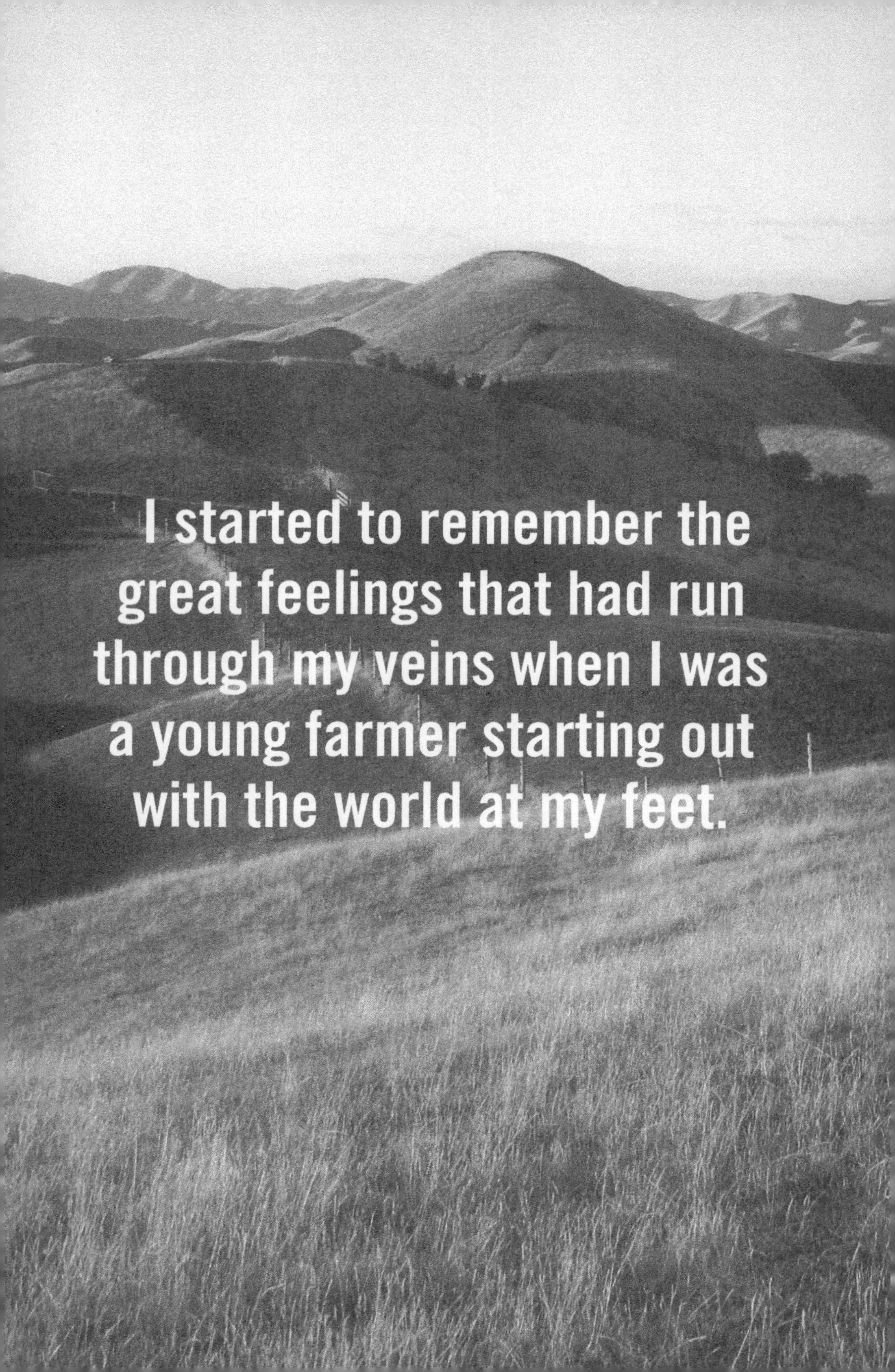

I started to remember the great feelings that had run through my veins when I was a young farmer starting out with the world at my feet.

21

LEADING FOR CHANGE

If we are to strive and to achieve solutions we can't simply dream; we must define relevant actions, and then we must act. It suits me perfectly, because I just love to get things done. I never want to stand on the sidelines while some other bastard does all the work. I get in there. I want to drive it from up the front.

One of my great strengths is that when I get something – when something makes sense to me, like the lucerne – I'm on to it. I see it; I'm ready to wade in and start working. It's a strength, but it's also a problem: sometimes I take off full-tilt down the track, and then I look back and wonder, where's everyone else? I'm like a hound on the scent, but no one else can see what I'm following.

So the moment Don Ross offered engaging language, I was in. Unlike our critics, he was presenting the possibility of a solution to our problem. I didn't know it then, but what was happening in my head ticked all the boxes for how to deal with depression: create hope, connect with people, learn new things; take notice of what's going on in the world; stay focused on what you can influence. It all begins with that word 'hope', as without hope, nothing else follows. Now, I saw an opportunity to act. And I guess it finally came down to this: I accepted I needed to change.

After one of our first meetings, Don Ross thrust a booklet at me.

'Here,' he said. 'Read this if you have time.'

It was called *Growing for Good: Intensive farming, sustainability and New Zealand's environment*; at that time it was a brand new publication by the Commission for the Environment. I read it cover to cover – couldn't put it down. Holy hell. It completely convinced me of what we needed to do. It was a new road. It talked about sustainability, about natural capital – the very first time I'd ever heard that term.

The key message, the idea that lodged in my tired old brain, was that I had been working so hard to change my environment to suit my farming system; instead, I needed to change my farming system to suit the environment.

Landcare had already worked with many rural people, and they knew there were scientists of all kinds who could help us, if we could get the funding to bring them in. So for the next year, that became our mission: to refine our goals and set up the parameters of our project.

There have been many times over the years when I wished we'd chosen a catchier name than the Starborough Flaxbourne Soil Conservation Group; it's a terrible mouthful. But it described what we were about: we recognised the damage we were doing to our landscape, and we sought ways to improve our stewardship of the land. While the project was centred on Grassmere, the area between the Awatere and Flaxbourne rivers, we always intended that it deliver usable outcomes to the entire dryland farming community of New Zealand.

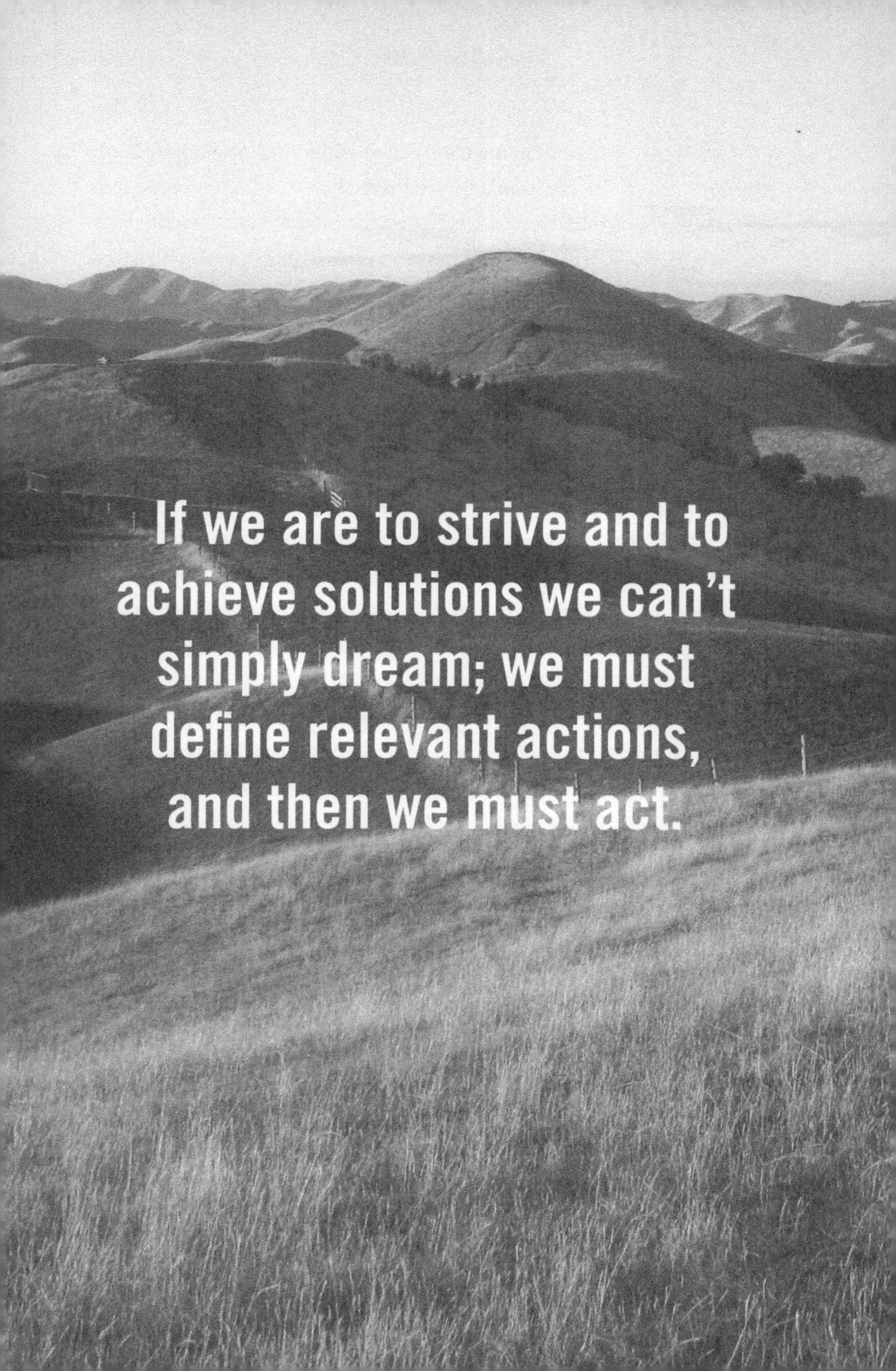

If we are to strive and to achieve solutions we can't simply dream; we must define relevant actions, and then we must act.

Landcare prepared a massive submission and we applied for funding from the Sustainable Farming Fund, which chipped in $250,000. We applied to the Marlborough Council and I went along to present our submission. The mayor, eyeing this huge, thick wad of paper, looked over his glasses and said, 'Mr Avery, you don't need to read the whole submission.'

'Your worship,' I replied, 'I had no intention of reading any of it seeing as it's been supplied in written form. I am certain that every councillor will have read the entire thing.' It was that bloody thick I knew they wouldn't have. I offered to show them a PowerPoint instead, and they were so impressed they gave us everything we asked for – which, in their case, was basically moral support for the journey. We wanted to make Grassmere great again, and they stumped up with printing facilities, mapping facilities – whatever background assistance we needed.

By the end of 2004 we were ready to go. My farm, Bonavaree, and two others were chosen as the models for the project. I couldn't wait to get started. And so from 2005 through to the very end of the project in June 2008, my mind and my world were blown apart.

We had the specialists. Soil scientist Richard Hunter, social science researcher Katie Nimmo, farming systems analyst Graeme Ogle, landscape consultant Paul Millen, dryland shrubs and plants expert Barrie Wills, and climate change scientist Gavin Kenny.

On climate issues, we also got input from NIWA's Alan Porteous. He offered to climate-model our farm back to 1890. 'What good would that be?' I wondered. But the modelling was amazing, giving me deep insights into our past and the stories my grandfather and father had told me. The old boys always reckoned they had weathered more, of course, but NIWA's modelling confirmed I had gone through the worst drought in recorded times, and that knowledge helped me feel a little better.

We created a system that's like a circular jigsaw puzzle: a continuous, year-round approach of interconnected land use, rotating crops and herds, using methods that trap in the ground what moisture we get in one season for use in the next.

It sounds so simple, but radical change is often like that: once you've done it, it seems so obvious. How often do you hear people say, 'The answer was right in front of me, if only I'd had the eyes to see'? The truth is, when we're sunk in our difficulties, immersed in our habitual way of doing things, we often can't see. But if we get another pair of eyes on the job, if we grab a helping hand, that's when change becomes possible.

My friend Matt Hood, a rural manager with Rabobank, recently asked me: 'Doug, did you know you can train a flea?'

'No, I had no idea that you could do this,' I replied.

'A flea,' he informed me, 'can jump a hundred times its own height.'

'I know that,' I told him, but I conceded it was extraordinary.

'Imagine if we could jump a hundred times our own height,' he said.

I thought about that for a minute. Then I waited for him to get to the point.

'You can put a flea in a deep bowl and cover it with plastic wrap,' he said. 'The flea will jump and hit the clear wrap. He will jump again, and again, and after a while he will stop, never to try again. He has learned that jumping can no longer create a result, so he has given up. You can remove the wrap and the flea will never try to jump out.'

'Really,' I replied.

Matt finally got to the point. 'Fleas are like people,' he said. 'So many of us try things and give up because we hit the same ceiling. Those who win give that jump another go. While they're sitting in the bottom of the bowl they are planning and plotting. *Maybe one day the ceiling will change*, they think. They get ready for that possibility.'

I considered my life at Bonavaree. It fitted the story so closely. Nothing I had been doing was bringing me any reward, so, like the flea, I had given up. Lucerne, and now the SFSCG, gave us the chance to jump out of the ryegrass bowl and into a new level.

So I ask you as you read: have you got another jump in you? Maybe you need some positive voices around to help you, and if you feel it's a risk to try, just ask how much risk there is in *not* trying.

My story is about my life as a farmer; my concern is farming systems. Your story may be unfolding somewhere in the urban jungle. It really makes no difference. The steps I took that carried me out of my dark years were all signposted along the well-trodden path towards mental wellness. I'm a farmer; you may not be. But I believe the steps I needed to take are no different to those available to anyone who's got stuck in their life and is sitting there hating and blaming themselves and the world.

For all those dark years, I'd hidden myself away from people. One by one I'd rejected everyone who was important to me. I was your classic Man Alone, hating the world and thinking I could do it all myself. I'd even taken some of that attitude along to that first meeting with Don Ross – no one was readier than I to chuck the whole thing in the rubbish basket before we'd even begun. But with his engaging, inclusive, non-accusatory manner, Don began the process that I describe as softening my arteries. I softened my attitude: I said 'yes' to what was on offer. I opened the door, and in came a bunch of people who helped me right across the spectrum of my life. Primarily I'm talking about farming – that was the bit that had become too tough for me. But because I'm so solutions focused, once I felt hopeful and energised about my work again, everything else began to flourish.

I'm terrified of the isolated place that I went to in the past. I'm now a collaborator. To this day, I employ a mentor to keep me thinking straight, and I bring people into my life all the time. You'll never find me working independently again. I love the culture of the business that we've grown.

22

FUTURE FOCUS

In recent years, Wendy and I travelled to Greece and, of course, toured around the historic sites. It was fascinating, but I stared out the window of the bus and became preoccupied with the state of Greece today. I shook my head at their agriculture. They wasted water and they had very poor water conversion to plants. Their economy was in tatters and their social fabric had collapsed. Meanwhile, they spent their whole time celebrating what they used to be, and they weren't looking forward to the future.

This is applicable to all of us in our lives. I don't want people to say 'once, we were this'. It's about working together to create the future.

The futurist Thomas Frey explains it by saying that, as a society, we are 'negative geared'. We look to the past for our thinking, because the past is very knowable. We've lived our life there, after all. But, in a way, that's like walking backwards into the future.

If I wanted to, I could reverse my car to Blenheim, but it would be a very high-risk way of travelling. Instead, the safest and fastest way to travel is by driving forward; my main point of vision is my large, wide windscreen, but I can be mindful of my rear-vision mirror, which allows me to look back when I need to. We won't be living our lives in the past; we'll be living our lives in the future.

The future creates the present. When you can see where you want to go, you will get there. When you see where you want to be, you will make the decisions now around how to make that journey.

For me, the entire Starborough Flaxbourne project was about learning to look to the future, not to the past; and above all it was Johnny Peter who turned me around to see my way ahead.

I have a photo of Johnny that I love and often show in my presentations. When I was invited to speak at farmers' events around the country, I'd get Johnny to come with me. We'd spend days in the truck, telling stories. He knew everything about everyone. One time, we were travelling to Ranfurly down in Central Otago when he suddenly said: 'Stop the truck!' He hopped out and stood there, gazing at the beautiful landscape. That's when I took the photo – a back view of Johnny, looking out to the far distance. It's the perfect photo, because what he showed me was vision. He showed me what I could achieve when I look forward. He helped me understand that the future creates the present.

Johnny Peter died in November 2007 – the Landcare booklet documenting the Starborough Flaxbourne Soil Conservation Group was dedicated to his memory. He's remembered for his courage in confronting the damage being done to Marlborough's dryland hill country by drought, and his mana in taking the Starborough Flaxbourne farming community with him on a search for solutions.

At the outset of the SFSCG, Johnny was chairman and I was his deputy. As the work progressed, Johnny stepped down and I took his place. He had no computer skills and was finding reporting and other parts difficult.

One day he rang me. There was some little issue going on between him and Don Ross – the kind of thing that happens on every committee there's ever been – and Johnny was hopping: 'That bloody Don Ross, he's gone too far. I'm coming down to your place and we'll construct a letter and send it to him. Pull him back into line . . .'

Johnny arrived and was unusually agitated. It was storm in a teacup stuff to me, but soon we had a letter drafted. 'Do you want me to scan it and email it?' I asked.

'Like bloody hell,' he replied. He didn't trust computers. 'Get me an envelope and stamp. Make it two stamps! I want it FastPost.'

Before we sealed the envelope I took the letter to my office and scanned it, and emailed it to Don in Christchurch. Johnny left, stopped at Seddon and posted the letter, then proceeded to Dashwood, where he lived, fifteen minutes away from Bonavaree. As he entered his house the phone was ringing. It was Don Ross to address Johnny's concerns.

It wasn't long before my phone rang. It was Johnny. 'I've always been down on the postal system,' he said, 'always thought they were a pack of useless buggers, but hell that FastPost is good. That bloody Ross was ringing when I got home.'

Every visit from Johnny was a gem, and Wendy and I loved his company. In his final four years I basically stole him from his family. He stepped in after Dad died, mentoring me in his humble way, and filling me with gratitude. He had plenty of time, and I had plenty of interest. I would come home and his little car would be on the front lawn. By this stage his marriage had ended and he loved a bit of female company and care, and Wendy's morning or afternoon teas suited Johnny well.

Together, he and I travelled, we talked and we laughed.

If it hadn't been for him, with his future focus, the SFSCG would never have happened.

It makes me think of Dad, and how, in effect, when I insisted on our buying Glen Erin, I turned him from looking back to the past to focusing on the future. It was only then that he began to be happy again. And that's what Johnny did for me when he invited Landcare to join us, and we set up the SFSCG.

He made me feel lucky, and everything became exciting – and I now realise that I love being with others who feel that way, too. When we focus on the future, our collective enthusiasm builds energy and purpose – like forcefields of energy transmitted from one person to the next.

23

FLYING THE 'V'

I see them sometimes when I'm out in the paddock, a wedge of geese flying in a V against the sky. And I hear them honking and crying, their voices spilling through the air.

The reason they fly in that formation is that each goose gets seventy-one percent more flying distance, thanks to the reduction of wind resistance. It's like drafting with a bike – it creates the opportunity for greater flying distance for the whole group. This is where collaboration comes in.

But the one out the front gets no assistance at all – nothing but positive reinforcement from its team-mates. The honking is them saying: 'You bloody good thing, fly! We're right behind you!' They're positively honking each other to fly further.

They're in an organised group and they're collaborating for the advantage. What's more, when one begins to tire, another one will take its place and it can fall back and enjoy the lift the collaboration is bringing.

Do you ever think about what kind of language you use with your friends and in your business? Are you saying to them, 'I think you can work harder,' or are you saying, 'Fly to the front, give us a yell when you're tired'?

It's a simple thing, but that's what I call teamwork. That's what I call relationship building. The geese use their relationships and their organisation to advance their own opportunities in life.

We had a situation here on the farm where Fraser had been away, and our stock manager had been taking care of things – flying the front. Then he had an emergency and needed some leave. It was a busy time, and there was pressure on all the farm staff.

Could we say to him, 'Nah, we've got so much pressure on here at the moment. You've got to fly in the front because we can't afford for you to pull back'?

No, that's the wrong thing to do.

The right thing to say was: 'You go and get yourself right. Maybe we can't fly as far this year.'

And then what happened was, the rest of the guys were still here working at seven o'clock that evening. It was as if they had said: 'We'll hop up and fly the front for you.'

Given the fact that he'd been flying the front so strongly, it was much wiser to allow him to take that time for something important. And these other guys, if you got out there last night and asked, 'Is it a problem that you're out here working at this time?' they would have said, 'No, we're covering for our mate. We're flying the front.' There would have been positive honking out there.

Isn't it good? Imagine how this world would be if we could keep turning people to that more positive, collaborative approach. But if you have a goose in the back who's coasting along saying, 'He's a sucker, that fellow at the front,' or who decides the goose at the front is useless and so he flies off on his own, it's lost.

It's all about relationships and collaborations. Penguins provide another example when they use their collective body temperature to survive the incredible winters of Antarctica. The key word: *together*.

I was invited to the National Agricultural Fieldays at Mystery Creek in Hamilton, and had done three days in a row on the main stage. At the end, a guy waited for me to finish talking to the others who crowded around, and then he asked for some time with me. He cut straight to the mustard. 'Last week I tried to suicide,' he told me. He was from a large farm in Australia, a man with many responsibilities who had, quite simply, burnt himself to a cinder. 'I thought I'd better get myself out here because I'm a danger to myself. I've walked up and down this place for two days and all I've been doing is looking at my feet. I haven't seen anything, haven't enjoyed anything. I heard you mention the word suicide when I was walking past here and I thought, I'll sit down and listen. I've never met anyone that understands where I am and I need to talk to you.'

I found a quiet room where we could talk.

'I've let my whole family down,' he said. As he talked, it became obvious to me that he was exhausted.

'You've been flying at the front for too long,' I told him. 'You haven't let your family down at all. It's just that you've run out of steam. I've been to that place: you can't fly the front any more.'

I asked him whether he'd told his wife.

'Hell, no,' he said. (It's always *Hell, no.*) So back home, in his relationship, a huge gap had opened up, bringing great loneliness on each side.

When he understood that, he realised he hadn't let his family down, but he could see now what the problem was, and it gave him the understanding to make changes. He needed to let others know what he was going through. He needed to step back and let others fly into the space he was still trying to occupy even as he realised he was failing.

It's all about communication – about not forgetting, even when you're flying up the front, that there's a team behind you, encouraging you, ready to give you a break when you let them know you need one. When one man falls, another one rises.

My family is probably like yours. Some things stay the same, but life evolves and takes us with it. The older generations watch the new generations stepping up, making changes, taking their turn at the sharp end of the V.

I've seen some families where the older generation won't make way for the new – the old guy keeps flying the front and the young ones never get the chance to step up. In our industry in particular, old men have had a wonderful record of destroying their sons. But in our family that hasn't happened. I'm proud of the way we've passed the baton, one generation to the next. Old men and women have stepped aside and given space to those coming along.

When Ern and Amy Avery stepped aside for Graham and Joyce, they had done twenty-six years of flying the front. Ern was a gambler and an ideas man. He passed the farm to his son Graham, a stabiliser and a doer, a precise, risk-averse person who, with Joyce, had thirty-four years flying the front. Then I came along with my bust-the-door-down energy, and Wendy and I flew the front for thirty-one years. We were blessed by positive honking from those who flew with us. We still live on the farm, but the baton has passed to Fraser and Shelley. And Fraser is so like my father; he's calmed things down and turned it all into runs on the board.

We Averys have had smooth baton changes. We have been lucky

It's all about communication – about not forgetting, even when you're flying up the front, that there's a team behind you, encouraging you, ready to give you a break when you let them know you need one. When one man falls, another one rises.

that the baton has never been dropped, that changes have been able to happen in a way that creates strength. I believe we all celebrate the growing of abilities, and each generation is more capable and better equipped to face tomorrow.

Our business is absolutely flying now, and without doubt a major part of that is the ability of our son, Fraser – the fourth generation of our family to farm at Bonavaree.

Dad died in 2004, just as the SFSCG was getting underway. He never knew the astounding changes we were embarking on.

My last time with him out on the farm was just before he died. We both knew it was his last visit; we were doing what had been our joint love for the last time together. I'm an emotional man and so was Dad, so the tears were flowing, and so was the laughter. We drove to the top of a hill and I stopped the truck and we talked about the journey, the great times we had had and the new direction he was starting to see emerge. He had opposed aspects of our change, but at one stage he made the comment: 'Doug, I have never seen the lucerne looking so good.'

Shortly before this I got him to plant his final tree, a liquidambar. Today I would have planted something native – I was still thinking in yesterday then; hadn't yet met Paul Millen or embarked on that wonderful journey of discovery and respect. But it's all part of my life's path, and the liquidambar is doing fine – although, like all trees in our area, it's growing very slowly. It's like my Dad, small but tough, and it stands in the middle of the original Bonavaree block where we grow the very best lucerne.

As he sat up in bed in the hospice, on one of his last days of life, he asked me to bring him his boots.

'What do you want your boots for?' I was completely bemused.

'Look at that garden outside there,' he said, nodding at the window. 'What a bloody mess. If I'm feeling a bit better in the morning I'll weed that garden.'

That's the kind of guy I was brought up by. How bloody inspirational is that? On his deathbed and he's still a servant. That was huge for me.

My sister Alison, who married a Maori guy, rang up the morning after he'd died. 'What's going to happen now?' she asked. 'My lot don't understand your lot's way of dealing with this.' She expressed a desire to have a tangi. I'd never been involved with anything like that, apart from when Michael McKee's body was brought home after the tractor accident. But I knew the presence of Michael's body had been very helpful in my grief.

'I'd love to bring him home,' I told Alison. Wendy agreed and Mum, although very uncomfortable, did too.

It was the right thing. Over three days we kept him company, gathering around his casket and covering off the stories of his life, and it seemed he was right there with us in complete harmony. So many people, some of them we barely knew, turned up at our farm and shared their own grief about their loved ones with us. It was an amazing time.

Then one morning I woke up about half past four, made a cup of coffee. I crouched down beside the coffin. I lifted the lid and put it up against the wall. I had the coffee in my hand, then I put it down and put my hands on Dad's head and I could feel the heat from my hands going into his body. I felt the real presence of connectedness.

It was like the transfer of leadership, a time to stand up. The days of asking for guidance were gone.

When it was time for the funeral, we filled his coffin up with lucerne seed and bits and pieces. I drove to town in the hearse with the undertaker, and I noticed that as we passed through the streets, people would run inside at the sight of the hearse. I thought it was interesting, and so far from the peace I now found within myself after the powerful energy of the tangi.

At the cemetery, a detachment from the air force gave a three-gun volley that rang across the district. I don't think I've ever felt so proud.

Ten days after that, I gave my first speech to the SFSCG. I was a man on a new mission. Dad knew that it was starting, but he never knew about what happened here. Mum will tell him when she gets there. It's a nice thing to believe, isn't it?

24

THE WHY

'Our vision is far grander than just saltbush, just troubled hills or just valley floors. It's about moving thinking, preserving our natural capital, moving our farming systems to long-term sustainability; not just sitting around waiting for rain.'

I wrote that as I sat in a plane high above the Tasman in March 2005. I was returning from Australia, where I had witnessed land degradation beyond belief, and now I fully realised we were fighting for something huge – our very existence.

It was around that time that I first met Graeme Ogle, a farm systems analyst assigned to me as part of the SFSCG.

Why do I do what I do? I assumed I knew, but it turned out I didn't have a clue.

Graeme came down to the farm and I showed him around. I was pretty proud of the way I'd finally managed to get some cover on my hillsides after five or six years of them being completely bare. Graeme looked at them with the opposite of admiration.

'I can't understand why you waste so much feed on these hills,' he said.

'I don't know why you've been asked to work on this project,' I responded. 'The sooner I get you back to the airport, the better.'

And I pretty much booted him off the property. I couldn't understand why he was part of this project when he was obviously so ignorant. Here we were with decimated areas and all I knew was that I wanted to cover them up so I didn't feel so bad. I thought I was moving us forward; I felt he was insulting my entire history.

He went back to the airport with his tail between his legs, but he sent me an email a few days later. He said, 'I really want to be involved in this project.'

Fortunately, I gave him another chance, and he turned out to be the most valuable person that was involved.

He introduced me to the question that's now at the core of everything I do: Why? I never used to ask myself that question. I was just totally involved at the physical edge of farming.

It was initially very uncomfortable for me to be challenged about why I did what I did. Graeme would say: 'Why do you run so many cows? Why have you got all this breeding stock? Why have you got a system that doesn't fit the natural curves of what nature is offering you on this farm?'

'That's what we've always done,' I replied.

'It doesn't make any economic sense,' he'd say. 'It's not making any environmental sense. It's not making any social sense.'

It's not easy being challenged like that. He was essentially challenging me on my whole history. There's nothing more destabilising than having your entire belief system disrupted. But because I knew I needed to change, I opened my ears and my heart and tried not to be defensive. I soon stopped being uncomfortable, and this became the most exciting process I've ever been involved in. I was encouraged to run everything that we did through the mincer. Suddenly I got it: *Why?* I became like a two-year-old child: why do we do this, why do we do that? People were saying, 'Can't you shut up and stop asking why?'

Graeme Ogle involved us in Farmax, a software system designed to help farmers plan, monitor, review and analyse their farm operations. It provided the structure for us to start measuring what we did. We could at last see exactly how much money we made out of each part of our business, including the different values that we could convert from different plants. When we started measuring everything, then we were able to ask why, and begin to find profitable answers.

'You've got the hardest feed-supply and feed-demand curve I've ever experienced in all my years in consulting because you're attacking it in the wrong way,' he told me.

Under the old system we nearly always ran out of feed just when we most needed it. Lambs would be born early spring, with main production time in September, October November, December. So there'd be a huge feed demand from hungry, lactating ewes. Once the lambs were weaned and put to pasture the race was on to get them heavy enough for the meatworks – but often this was just as the summer dry was settling in and feed was drying up. At that point, under the old system, we would feed out the lucerne we'd cut and conserved the previous spring. We would struggle to get the lambs up to weight, and sometimes have to sell them at a heavy discount to other farmers who had sufficient feed to finish fattening them – and they'd collect the full profit at point of kill. Meanwhile, the ewes would be struggling on the drought-stricken pastures to regain their own weight in the lead-up to the next mating season. So we were always behind, always borrowing from the coming year.

Over the years since I'd met Derrick Moot and begun growing lucerne for direct-grazing, things had improved. Lambs were ready sooner, ewes were healthier, and there was less pressure over the hot summer months. But I hadn't conceived of the shift as being a total system change. I was tinkering at the edges, but couldn't see it holistically. Now I was looking at exponential change. It was as if I had new eyes.

Ogle helped me analyse what was going on, and brought a quantitative approach to our understanding of the process at every step along the way.

'Every year you seem to run into the same problem,' he pointed out. 'Every year come Christmas time you've still got fifty per cent of your lambs that you need to finish with feed. If you fed those lambs properly they would be finished and off the farm, the money would be in the bank, and you could have a holiday.'

Ogle encouraged us to weigh our lambs at weaning, then weigh them again when they left the farm, and work out how much feed they had eaten in the interim. We quickly realised we weren't recovering the value of the feed they'd eaten; we were making no money over that interim period. We were actually working hard at an impossible task. Then when we got them finished we'd think we had finished the job, but they had actually eaten what would have been the next year's bounty, so the following year was already in ruins. We had this death-roll in the business and it was going on and on and on.

He kept asking us, 'Why do you do that?' and I couldn't answer him.

Now, with the new system that we evolved, ewes and lambs fed directly off spring lucerne, the animals reached their finishing weight very fast, and we could get them off the farm before the summer period even began.

Then we would spray out the green growing pasture while moisture levels were still high, which had the effect of trapping the remaining moisture in the plants' roots. Once you stop grass growth, water extraction from the soil almost ceases. Eighty per cent of the water in the ground at the time of spraying will stay there till early autumn when we resow. That then means the new crops are fuelled by last spring's surplus water and start to grow even though the summer drought is still going.

By the time of the summer dry in January and February, the farm is carrying minimal stock, and the ewes – thanks to the lucerne – are already back up to good weights, in prime condition for mating. That in turn means our crops go into the winter strong, and pregnant ewes eat well and we get lots of strong lambs born in early spring. They in turn grow fast and finish before the next summer. It's a whole cycle of success, based on the storage and transfer of water from one season to the next.

The thing that we get most challenged on in our farming system is our use of Roundup. We use it to spray off a proportion of the lucerne at the end of spring to lie fallow over the summer. It's not ideal, but it's a major part of transferring water from one period to another, enabling us to take control of the water instead of the water controlling us.

When Roundup was first introduced we were told that you could drink it. A guy in the audience hopped up and said, 'Hold on. I've got a glass here. You show us how you do it.' The sales guy said, 'I'm talking figuratively.'

However, while I accept it's not ideal to use this stuff, we need to find another solution to trapping the moisture in the ground, and I don't know what that solution is. I want people to work with me for a solution. Meanwhile, it enables a system that has massively reduced our carbon footprint. In our situation, a paddock will get high-intensity change over a two-year period. Then it might go ten years in lucerne and never see anything like that again. There's this massive break where there's nothing but absolutely excellent stuff.

Now we work with the seasons, rather than against them. The lambs are born directly onto the lucerne pastures, and lactating ewes benefit from the high-octane feed. With such nourishment, the lambs put on an astonishing 380–400 grams a day – the New Zealand average is 174 grams – meaning they are ready to be weaned by December and sold, at above-average weight, for premium early-season prices.

By the end of 2005, just one year into the SFSCG, we were already reaping the benefits. We had shifted ninety per cent of our lambs off the farm by the end of November, and were thus spared the horror of trying to support and grow them in the scorching, parched months of summer. We were no longer at the mercy of the ever-oscillating weather.

Under Graeme Ogle's guidance, and thanks to the transparency afforded us by the Farmax system, we were able to build a new system around our lucerne. We were already stumbling towards this, thanks to Derrick Moot's encouragement and our change to lucerne direct-grazing, but we didn't have the conceptual framework to really make a go of it.

The sun, which had once been my biggest enemy and nearly killed me, is now my best friend. It's what grows our animals and plants. Our lucerne plants have great big, fat leaves that soak up the sun's energy through photosynthesis. When ryegrass gets dry, the first thing it does is fold its leaves around and get a waxy coat on so it doesn't transpire so much. That protects the plant the best it can, but its usability as a food source diminishes drastically. But with our legume system, as we dry out heading towards summer, the plants turn their leaves towards the sun and are energised, and our finishing ability accelerates.

Our animals are fat and sleek. They're bouncing off the walls in all this sunshine and with such good food. We're one of the most successful sheep and beef farms in this country, even though we farm in one of the most unfavourable areas. If we can do this, anyone can.

25

NATURAL CAPITAL

No problem is solved from the same consciousness in which it was created.

In my young days as a farmer I set out with my hand-held scrub-cutter to get rid of the manuka that was stopping the grass growing on the hills. It was hot work, and I paused for a cup of tea. Sitting on the hillside above a bushy gully, replenishing my energy, I surveyed my progress with satisfaction.

A couple of decades later, and I was back in the exact same place, this time with a spade in my hands. Hot work. I stopped for a cup of tea and suddenly remembered myself from all those years ago. What different work I was now doing. This time, I was planting . . . manuka! The same man, sitting in the same place, doing the complete opposite job.

I feel no bitterness towards my younger self, or towards my father and grandfather who taught me to farm in that old way. In their hearts they were fantastic carers of the land in the way they understood. But I understand differently now.

As a young farmer I saw no problem in letting the sheep and cattle poke around in the remnants of bush that still grew in our gullies. Riddling the bush with their tracks, they found their shade under the trees. But I hadn't realised they were eating all the seedlings, with the result that all our prevailing species were from a single generation. There was no chance of renewal.

As the SFSCG progressed, my eyes gradually opened to these processes, and to the true nature of capital. I had thought there was one kind of capital, represented by my farm's capital stock – my financial investment. Now I understand that financial capital is only one leg of the tripod. Equally important are the other two legs: environmental and social. Our environmental capital is of course our land, which supports our plants and animals. Our social capital is our people and ourselves – our well-being – and I have to be strong enough emotionally to take this challenge on, with all the complexities that come with it. I now hold these two capitals in higher regard than our capital stock.

Sustainability depends on all three legs being strong. It's like a stool: if you sit on a stool with only one or two legs, you'll go crashing to the ground. I will have no capital stock if my land and I aren't strong.

My awakening to the concept of natural capital came one day when I was walking around the farm with landscape consultant Paul Millen, another important person in our story. The hills were dry, of course, and my northern slopes were ravaged and ugly with tunnel erosion, but in some of the gullies were remnants of native bush. I used to call it 'scrub' – manuka, cabbage trees and so on. It's the kind of stuff the government used to pay farmers to clear. Now I call it biodiversity.

'If you tried to recreate that, Doug, it would cost at least $85,000 a hectare,' Millen told me.

I nearly fell over. I looked afresh at the stand of frowsy cabbage trees. It was as if I'd never seen them before. When Millen attached a monetary value to them, he grabbed my attention. He created a short cut to my head. But it wasn't long before I started to link these natural areas up to the deeper values of the system we were running.

Understanding this intertwined set of relationships – environmental, social, financial – has birthed my concept of holistic farming. I never liked to use that word 'holistic' because for me, it's associated with people who are grinding up cow horns, which will never be part of my energy. But now I think I want to reclaim the word 'holistic' – and why not? Farmers have a right to use it. It just means that every part of what we do is related to every other part, and that every part is understood in relation to the whole. A system. A dynamic agricultural system has no corners, no places that force us to stop, to back away, to lose our momentum. If we have smooth momentum it's the same thing as the fella who designed the wheel – just marvellous smooth progress, so much better than what he had before.

Early on in the SFSCG process, Don Ross got everyone – all the specialists – around the table and he told them: 'Every one of you, in every part of your work, will have to sign off your work with every other one of you. And until you've shown me how you integrated with everybody else here, I won't pay you.'

That was tough news to some of them, used to their own speciality and not to integration. But Ross insisted on it, and that was the value of our process. You can't have a holistic system if there are parts that don't link with other parts. This was the thought pattern that Don Ross insisted upon, and it was the key to our success.

One of the other great keys to the success of the SFSCG was the involvement of Barbara Stuart, the upper South Island facilitator for Landcare. She is a woman of guts and courage who had her own story of loss and recovery; one of her sons, Evan, was among the fourteen teenagers killed when the viewing platform collapsed at Cave Creek on the West Coast in 1995. She's been a spokesperson for those parents. Since then, she's been involved in some important environmental projects, and for the SFSCG she was the one who kept us on the road. She played the back and she ran the forecourt.

Barbara remembered me from the days when our sons played hockey together, although we'd never spoken. But back then she'd seen my grim face and understood I was one of a type: a farmer burdened by responsibility, the climate, too much outside my control, in danger of blowing my heritage. She understood all that well – she's a farmer herself – and saw it often, among farming men in particular.

It was her great skill to bring this group of rural people and scientists together, and to keep us together. She had empathy but also toughness. 'Doug,' she said to me once, when I'd been throwing my toys out of the cot over something, probably exhibiting some awful self-pity, 'there's a lot of energy gone into this project. You will behave yourself.'

We forged ahead. Understanding about integration and natural capital drove the big changes we made during the SFSCG process. For instance, we've protected our eroding hill slopes by planting them with stock fodder plants like drought-resistant saltbush and tagasaste. These have rapid growth rates and develop deep root systems. The tagasaste has the added benefit of providing food for bumblebees, which in their turn are important pollinators of our lucerne. The plants shade the soil, reduce ground temperatures and minimise evaporation. Over time, leaf litter and soil organic matter build up, which increases soil moisture holding capacity and stabilises eroding hill slopes. Once established, these plants can be grazed and provide stock shelter and shade.

We have done a lot of work to protect and restore the biodiversity of our area. South-east Marlborough has more biodiversity than the world-famous Marlborough Sounds, but it's under greater challenge, so being involved in preserving that was pretty special.

We identified and fenced off several natural areas, to protect them forever. In some of them we have planted thousands of trees. In one big gully, about thirteen hectares, we planted about 3000 natives around the periphery – an amazing story of conservation and renewal that I'm so proud to be part of. There's a species of totara called lowland totara, which had got down to only about five or six trees in the Flaxbourne gorge, where they'd been protected by the steepness and rockiness of that place. Working with Paul Millen, the Marlborough District Council set up a seed collection site there, and then we planted a heap of those lowland totara seedlings on our place. I will have well and truly rotted into the ground myself before there's anything spectacular there, because trees grow so slowly in this area; but as a result of that, those totara are now all over this part of Marlborough. We have gone a long way towards saving that particular species. And of course there's a lot of flax and cabbage trees and kowhai and all sorts of stuff up there and that's doing really well.

The area that I had once cleared of manuka, we placed under a QEII covenant and named it the Graham and Joyce Avery Wetland. We planted around 500 trees in there, and every time I visit I see the fresh young heads of new cabbage trees pushing up through the flax and manuka.

Our biggest natural area is about twenty-seven hectares, a gorge where sheep and cattle used to roam. We haven't even had to plant anything in there; we simply fenced it off to exclude the animals and now there's a massive regeneration of native trees. I look at all those

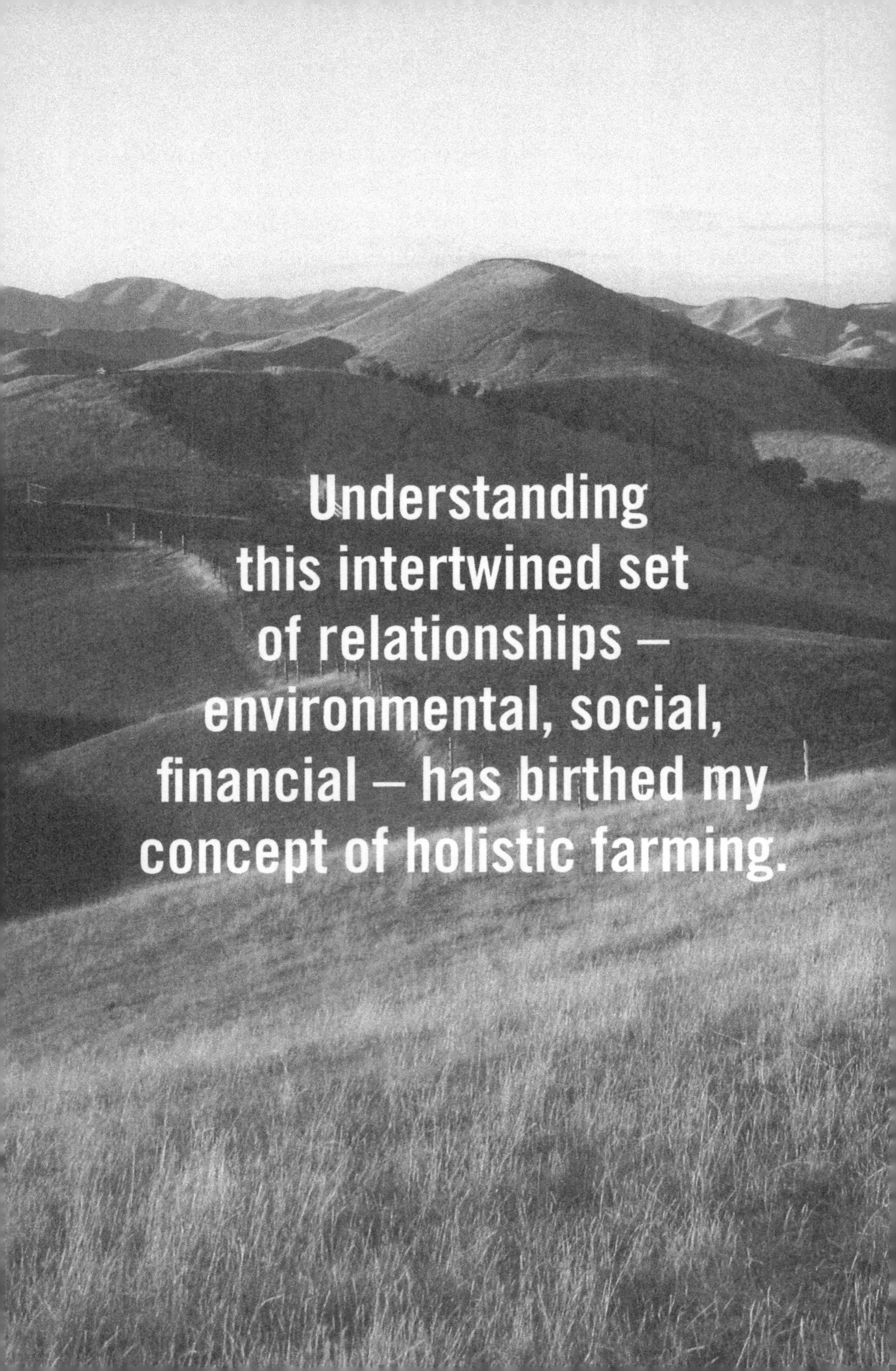

Understanding
this intertwined set
of relationships –
environmental, social,
financial – has birthed my
concept of holistic farming.

young plants growing and I realise that we've created a succession plan.

To me it's a corridor from the river up to the hills. The effect on the bird population has been significant: when it's calm you can hear their song, the sound of happiness. We've all got to have our feel-good places.

It's a corridor for bad things as well, such as pigs and deer, but we're tough on them. We periodically poison for possums and stoats, too, and they've had a bugger of a last ten years.

We're just grateful that there were systems enabling us to do this work. I was one of the first to sign up to the Significant Natural Areas Project with the Marlborough District Council and the government; the deal is that we each pay one-third to preserve special areas. That was quite an enticement for me to get involved. It would have been too expensive to manage on my own, and I probably wouldn't have done it. I immediately got comments from other farmers: 'You'll regret this; every bastard will think they own your farm.' And I thought, well, if my farm's exciting enough – better, a nicer place to be – everyone will want to try and own it; it wouldn't worry me if my capital value lifted significantly! Doing this environmental work has increased the farm's value by every measure you can think of.

Over my lifetime people have referred to this area in some pretty disparaging ways. But I am honoured to have had the character to stay here and to try to make it better. The world thrives when people have the courage to take their own circumstances and make the most of them, in a way that's complementary to those around them. That's like biodiversity in the brain, isn't it?

It's easy to get overwhelmed by the challenges that confront us. My job is not to tell you or anyone else how to run your lives or your business. But I can tell you what I've done, and hope that my story will inspire others. I love to work with people and the land to build capacity for a better future, and I am so proud of our achievements here in conserving and enhancing our natural capital. As a business operator, I can't operate if I'm not successful in all three fields: environmental, social and financial.

Today, the whole system that we run here has a peaceful coexistence with reality. The people on the ground can now attend more acutely to the points that they can actually influence. I don't believe there's any difference between an agriculture system or a business in town or a home life or anything. When people have a better understanding of their circle of influence as opposed to being at the mercy of things beyond their control, they can apply their meaningful time so much more accurately. That creates the learning experience and the calmness and the relationships – the whole nine yards.

I want to be able to tell a story about this farm which is okay. I feel good that we've got things like our regeneration projects going on. I now know that in twenty or thirty years' time it's going to be a whole lot better than it is. Time will sort it out.

In the old days, when people asked me what area of the farm was effective, I always said we had a hundred hectares that was ineffective in terms of farming, but now I say there's none that's not effective in its own way. Every square inch of this business is part of our wholeness.

26

CIRCLE OF INFLUENCE

Talking at Waikato Stadium one day, I happened to tell the crowd that I was captain of the Rural Sad Bastards Club. Everyone laughed, but one guy – a fellow who runs a large farming operation but was struggling at the time – was very taken by my talk and language.

Great idea, he thought, and he did the same – he set up a group, calling themselves 'The Sad Bastards Club'. They meet once a month to share stories, chat, have one drink and download. Apparently it is very popular. Men are learning to manage their once taboo emotional selves. Hopefully, this guy and his friends will move on to complete a very happy time on this earth, enjoying the fruits of life.

One day, one man . . . it's contagious.

Change is what I'm about. But we have to know what we can change, and what we can't.

The things we worry about can take up the whole world. If you draw a circle and put inside it everything that you're concerned about, it's likely to be a great big circle.

Farmers are always worried about the value of the dollar; it's always too high or too low. If they're buying a tractor it's too low; if they're selling stuff it's too high. During my presentations, I ask them: 'Is there anyone here that's big enough in their capacity of sales to influence the value of the New Zealand dollar?' The silence is resounding.

One day I was speaking to Landcorp, the state-owned farming enterprise that owns 140 farms around New Zealand. I asked the CEO of Landcorp: 'You're the biggest farmer in New Zealand. If you got all sulky-dog and said, "We're not going to play this game any more," and you stopped producing product altogether, would it affect the value of the dollar?'

'No.'

'Is there anyone here bigger than Landcorp?'

'No.'

Another thing that farmers are always worried about is the weather. All my life it's been too hot, too dry, too wet, too cold. It's always too something or other. So I asked the same roomful of farmers and agribusiness apparatchiks: 'Is there anyone in the room tonight who can affect the weather? Has anyone got a wee connection upstairs?'

No. Neither, it turned out, could this room full of people do anything about the next Rugby World Cup, despite it being a top concern among farmers.

Terrorist attacks, global politics . . . worrying about all these things uses up massive amounts of our human energy. Together they make up our circle of concern.

I used to worry about absolutely everything. I burnt myself out; I felt burnt out every hour of every day. When someone is depressed, they don't have any confidence in their own ability to shape the world; they don't have any confidence in the ability of people around them. It's all too huge. No one can exist with any happiness inside the circle of concern.

Thankfully, there's another circle we can draw, and that's our circle of influence. That is, the things we have the capacity to do something about.

When I was at my lowest spot, my circle of influence was so small it wouldn't have been detected by a microscope. The drought had blinded me to the things I did have control over. My energy was destructively distributed over so many things that in the end I was totally lost. But when I began transferring my energy to things I could do something about, my circle of influence quite quickly began to grow: how can we make a litre of water produce a better result? What plants can we use that can manage on our limited water to get a better outcome? How can we produce feed to the quality and quantity that we need at particular times of year? What animals could we change?

We'd always bred Corriedale sheep; they're a dual-purpose animal, good for both meat and wool. But they're very skittish: if you clapped your hands near one that had just lambed, it would jump and run, and if the lamb was fit enough it would go, too, but if it wasn't the ewe would just leave it behind to die.

Now we use a new, composite breed that I call 'doofers': they do for us. They're dial-a-genetic – a mix of Romney, Texel, Finn and Coopworth – and they're basically designed to be milk factories. They free-lamb so we don't need to attend to them. Their udder formation is beautiful and the teats stick out so when the lambs are born they can get straight onto it. They are great mothers. To protect their lambs they will almost bark at a dog if it enters the paddock. Oh, all those wasted days lambing ewes and chasing dreams when I was young – and the joy to see how it's done today!

So our doofers are part of the change that happened when I started to focus on my circle of influence. Over the years, we changed nearly everything, one step at a time. I look at some of the people who are leading our industry, and the biggest change they've had in their life was when they changed the kind of tobacco they smoke in their pipe. They've never actually been through change like we've done. We changed the plants we used; we changed the animals; we changed the way we used our land. We changed the way we looked at what we did, so we don't call ourselves farmers of sheep or cattle; we're farmers of water.

Our limiting factor will always be the amount of water that we get. So one of the questions within my circle of influence was: how can we make more use of the tiny amount of water that falls on our land? As I'm documenting in this book, the answer didn't come straight away; it's fair to say that even the question itself took a few years to crystallise. But because I had begun working on the things I could change – switching from ryegrass to lucerne was the first of the changes – each step took me to the next step, the next line of questioning.

When you take the first step on your journey of change, others will follow. But nothing can happen until you take that first step.

Since I started concentrating on the things that I could influence, my circle of influence has never ceased growing. And because of my focus on achievable solutions, I have reaped the rewards. When I first put in the lucerne, I called our new system 'poor man's irrigation'; but it has become so successful that it's wealthy man's irrigation.

When you're depressed, everything looks bad. *Everybody's wrecking this country, everything's been done wrong.* Yet I can take you to thousands of places where nothing's been done wrong at all. It's all been done quite well. If you were to put your energy into something that would grow your circle of influence, what could you achieve?

In my old way of doing things I would look at a problem and it would double before my eyes. If I have a worry now, I look for a solution straight away. And if there's no obvious immediate solution, I use a strategy offered by Dr Tom Mulholland of Farmstrong called 'twigging'. That's where, when you feel an emotion like anxiety or anger, you ask yourself: Is this thought True? Is it Worth It? And is this thought helping me to achieve my Goals? (TWIG). I put it into my own words, and it helps me break a problem down into manageable parts. Is the emotion real? Will solving this make me happy or better? What's the best possible position that we could take? Out of all the stuff that's on the board in front of me, which is the piece that I have to concentrate on *now*?

There are events that happen in everybody's lives that are just rotten beyond rotten, but figuring out your circle of influence is a way of moving forward. I want to influence people to do this kind of thinking – to grab hold of some of these simple little tools that make such a difference to life. People tend to be impressed with people who are doing stuff, and that's how the circle of influence grows.

All these tools are parts of a puzzle that fit together. I've already talked about letting our vision of the future determine our lives in the present: for instance, here I am now and in five years' time I want to be here, and in ten years' time here. When you think in this way, you are immediately brought within your circle of influence. What can you do now to get you to that place? Do you have to respond? Is this within your circle of influence? If it is, then be clear and decisive about what you can do.

If not, then let it go.

27

CRYSTAL-CLEAR GOLD

I have a dream of selling beautiful Marlborough spring lamb to the world as premium Christmas lamb. Our lamb is divine: it grows fast and, like anything that grows fast, it's sweet and delicious. The story goes like this:

> *We're bringing this absolute delight to your Christmas plate. This lamb is so fresh it's almost jumping, and it's grown in the fresh spring air under the amazing endless sunshine of Marlborough. It's here for you for Christmas in this cold, cold winter place that you live in . . . Could we also recommend a bottle of Marlborough Pinot Noir? And can I mention that our world-famous Sauvignon Blanc is grown just across the road under the same sunshine . . . And why not some flaky salt to go over the top of your delicate lamb – beautiful solar salt from the pristine lake of Grassmere . . .*

What a story! At Bonavaree we have our own story: of farming with nature, not against it; reducing our environmental footprint; improving our efficiency; farming in a more holistic way. Stories are so important: they can grow our market perhaps more than any other influence.

What about the story of our country? Look at our incredible gifts: we still have some of the cleanest water in the world, highly fertile lands, stable governance and incredible beauty. I would love to see us telling this story through high-value, boutique products, rather than the volume-above-value, quantity-above-quality mindset that dominates agricultural production at present. The cornerstone for the future of New Zealand agriculture is value above volume, and quality above quantity. There's so much opportunity in that space.

Water is at the heart of my story, and it's at the heart of the New Zealand story. According to the World Bank, we have over 72,000 cubic metres of renewable water per person; compare that with Australia, with around 20,000, or China with only 2000. Yet it's water, and the fight over how we should be using this precious commodity, that lies at the heart of the bitter divisions opening up in this country.

On Bonavaree water is not plentiful, so there is a high value on it and we have learnt to use it very efficiently. In fact, I claim that we are now the most efficient farm in New Zealand in relation to water use. Recognising water as a valuable natural commodity was central to developing a new and more sustainable farming system for Bonavaree, and it all began when Derrick Moot suggested to me that I was 'a farmer of water'.

It takes some 10,000 litres of water to make a kilogram of lamb. But if that lamb is grown where the rainfall is retrieved by lucerne's giant tap roots, allowing nature to release it into the delicious fodder that sheep and cattle love to eat – rather than pouring water onto the land through expensive irrigation systems – well, there's no other thing we could do better on this land. We convert that natural water into product and, in our case, we have recently doubled the value return of that water.

Other parts of New Zealand receive a lot of water from the sky; but the question is, how do we use it? How do we turn it into a better product and create greater value? Is it by making milk? Milk is behind much of New Zealand's wealth, yet it takes 1000 litres of water to make a litre of milk. In its early days the industry operated mainly where there was a lot of natural water, in places like Waikato and Taranaki. But then we thought: let's pump water, let's add nitrogen, and we turned once-dry areas into dairy pastures, and average pastures into even better pastures.

We add all that water, then we take the milk down to a big shiny factory with lots of stainless steel, we apply a whole lot of energy and we dry that milk out. Then we put the powder in a wee tin and send it to countries like China or India, often to places where they're shorter on water than we are. Guess what they do when it gets there? They add water to it to make it into milk again.

But if I go into the supermarket, the higher brands of water are more costly per litre than milk. Pumping huge volumes of water to make a product that is worth less than the starting product: it bends my mind. And yet New Zealanders are scratchy about selling water.

The town of Ashburton lies right in the heart of the Canterbury dairy industry. In 2015–16 many residents rose up in outrage at the local council's proposal to allow a resource consent to bottled water company NZ Pure Blue, who planned to extract 1.4 billion litres annually of pure artesian water to bottle and sell. That's 45 litres a second. It sounds like a lot, yet it's only equivalent to what one tiny dairy farm would take. This raised an important issue: what is the value we should put on our water, and on the use we make of it?

The key issue is the utilisation of the gifts we've got – in this case, water. It comes back to the big 'why': why do we do this? That's the question that should lie at the heart of any debate over our country's use of its natural gifts.

In China the base resource is people, and so they use very poorly rewarded people to create economic development. Our base resource is in the environment: it's water. It's so plentiful and cheap that we don't value it. What about fresh air? What greater gift could nature have given us? We take it for granted, yet Christchurch businessman Phillip Duval has found a lucrative market selling air, bottled fresh in the Southern Alps, to the Chinese, who are gasping in their polluted cities. A little breath of pure New Zealand air – for $28 a can.

If we focus on the value proposition, not the hard-work proposition, that's when we come up with the solutions. So: where is the value proposition in that water? To put it another way, if I hadn't started to ask questions about how we used water at Bonavaree, then we'd still be in that place of failure and despair.

In New Zealand we work hard and produce a lot. We feel we're serving our nation well when we work hard. But we don't always work smart. We can't compete with places like Australia, where farming is on a scale we can't possibly copy. On a massive wheat plantation, there may be only one employee who drives a harvester eight hours in one direction in a wheat paddock, and then he gets off and that's his shift. Another guy gets on and he drives back for eight hours in the other direction. There's dump points all the way along; no one even has to turn any corners. That's volume. Low-value, high-volume – that's how we create enough food to feed billions of people.

Their biggest farm is the same size as South Korea; another is equal in area to Israel. I met a guy at the Platinum Primary Producers conference who had a mandarin orchard. 'How big's your orchard?' I asked him. 'Not very big,' he said. 'Only four hundred and fifty hectares.' He was producing 70,000 to 85,000 tonnes of mandarins at $1500 a tonne. 'Not a bad little earner,' he said. He had other interests as well.

But Australian farmers pour on the fertilisers, including about two million tonnes of urea a year. When I was a boy, no one used artificial nitrogen. In the post-war agricultural boom, however, with new high-yield crops being developed, and cheap artificial nitrogen readily available for the first time in human history, farmers quickly became dependent. When droughts came, they realised they could still produce good crops if they added nitrogen. From that developed an addiction, really. 'Far out,' farmers said, 'I wonder what would happen if I put some on even though I haven't got a drought?' It turned out the equation's quite good. You grow more grass. You grow more and more and more grass.

A few years ago, clover root weevil swept from Northland and Waikato right down through the country. What that was, in my view, was clover's response to the artificial nitrogen being poured on those ryegrass and clover pastures. Clover is a legume, so it fixes its own nitrogen. But now it was being weakened by the artificial nitrogen. The plant's going, *Actually, I was here to fix the nitrogen but I don't understand what I'm doing any more. There's so much of it here. Where's it all coming from?* It's like we're saying to it, *We invited you to come along here to sing to the crowd today, but we've already got Elton John on stage.*

In a manner of speaking, the plant's left in a state of confusion as to what it's supposed to be doing and it's weakened. The clovers eventually disappear out of those dairy pastures. Then the farmer is in the position where he no longer has a choice: he must apply nitrogen, as otherwise he gets virtually no production at all. That's where the industry is right now.

Nitrogen run-off is now widely acknowledged as the 'bad guy', the culprit behind the pollution of our waterways. Also – and this is something we don't talk about much in New Zealand – the environmental cost of producing nitrogen fertiliser is very heavy. To make it, the nitrogen molecule is split to create urea, which takes a huge amount of fossil fuel. So: we either get our nitrogen from that very energy-expensive, fossil fuel-intensive process or, as Moot did, we ask: 'Can I come up with a better system that isn't going to be reliant on this nitrogen fertiliser?'

Our global food system is currently dependent on the use of artificial nitrogen; it's one of the reasons the world's population has increased from 1.2 billion people before 1940 to 7.5 billion today. The way I see it, we can't suddenly stop using it as there would be too much social dislocation, and people would starve. There's a massive amount of energy going into finding a solution now, and I feel hopeful that we'll go a long way in a reasonably quick time.

Nitrogen fertiliser inputs in New Zealand climbed from 50,000 tonnes to 400,000 tonnes between 1990 and 2006. Massey University reports that 750,000 tonnes was applied in 2014 to our pastoral land, with most of it applied to dairy farms. We've got a heap of farmers around New Zealand who have spent all their lives just pouring on artificial nitrogen.

But that's where nitrogen does its biggest damage, because it accelerates the exhaustion of soil carbons. Australia has used seventy per cent of the soil carbons that were in the land when European settlers arrived. What will happen when they've used a further seventy per cent of the thirty per cent they have left? Some farmers there are turning to hydroponics. Yet we don't really know yet what we're missing out on in food that's been grown without any contact

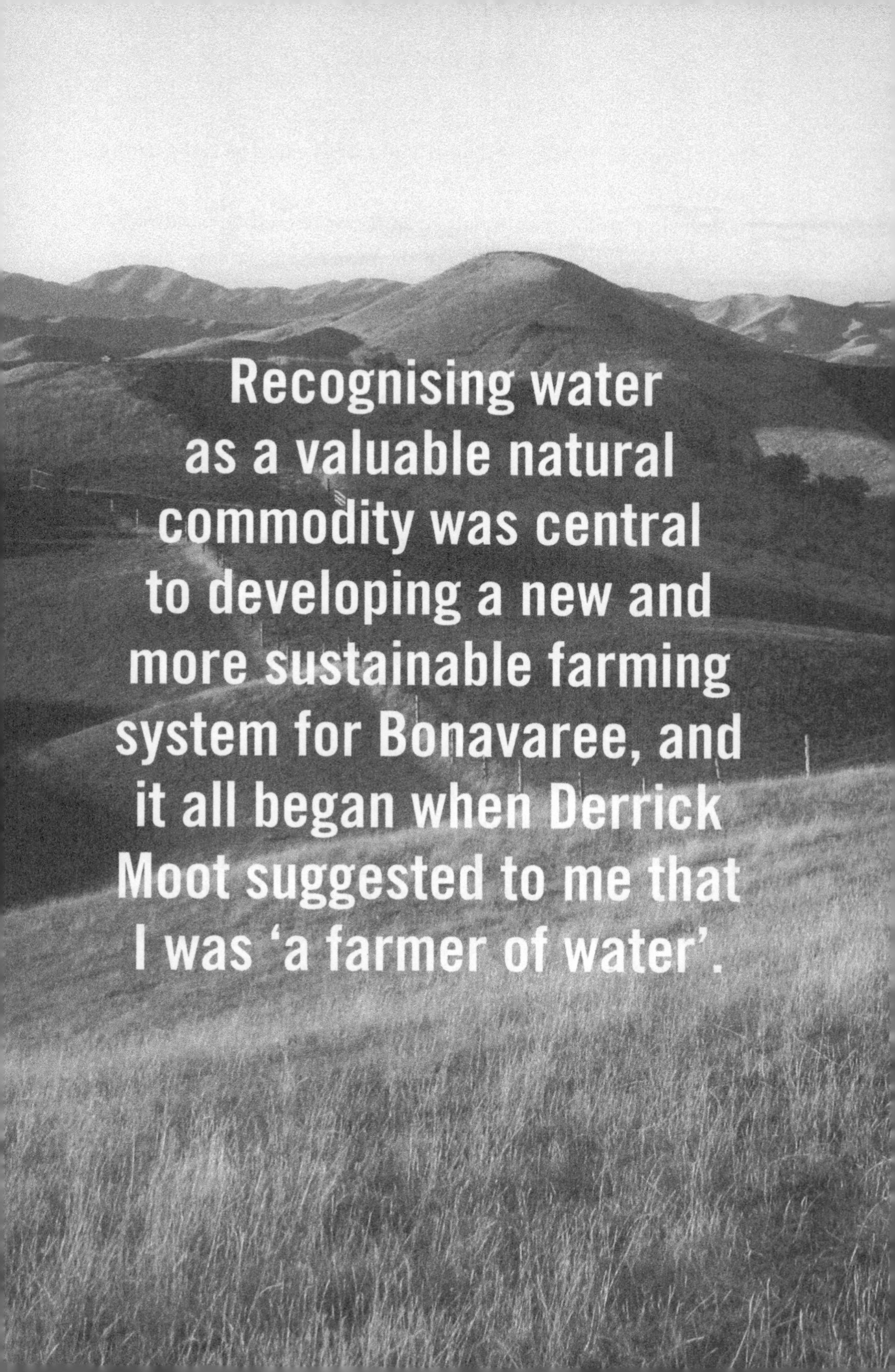

Recognising water as a valuable natural commodity was central to developing a new and more sustainable farming system for Bonavaree, and it all began when Derrick Moot suggested to me that I was 'a farmer of water'.

with soil. People want natural food – and what could be more natural than food raised on soil?

I want to promote natural nitrogen fixing because legumes, when they fix enough nitrogen to make themselves happy, stop fixing it. They know more about that stuff than we do; it just happens naturally.

When I say to farmers, 'How many of you fellas like turning away a gift when somebody gives you something? Do you say, nah, I don't think I should take that?', they laugh. Of course they love a free gift. I go to heaps of events where people hand out stuff to farmers and they all go, *I want one, I want two*. I say, 'So why are you so anti natural nitrogen? Why don't you want to take this gift?'

Legumes have a triple leveraging effect on production. Firstly, they double the value of a millimetre of water. If I get 300 millimetres of water here delivered by God each year, or 400, they effectively turn that into 600–800 millimetres, in terms of the dry matter I can produce on that land. Secondly, for every tonne of dry matter that a legume produces in a pasture you get 25 kilograms of natural nitrogen per hectare fixed for nothing. Thirdly, animals grazing on legumes will grow at twice the speed of animals on grass.

The environmental impact of that is nothing but positive. Animals, whether they're eating clover, lucerne or grass, have exactly the same greenhouse gas emissions. But if you halve the time it takes to finish an animal, its greenhouse gas emissions per unit of production are also halved.

Like I said earlier, our finishing weight for lambs has gone up to more than double the New Zealand average. That's incredible economic and environmental gain. But a lot of farmers reckon it's easier to go to the shed, pick up a bag of nitrogen and squirt it out the back of the tractor. The trouble with that is it's weakening their natural capital – and when one leg's bust, the stool falls over.

'Not everybody is open to change, not everybody needs to change, not everybody can change,' Derrick Moot says. He's had to learn patience, too. I changed because I had to change. But many farmers have a low mortgage and feel they're doing okay and don't want the extra work. *Yeah, I think it would work here but actually we're doing okay. Wait till my son comes home. He can do that.* I think we'll notice a big change as younger farmers come through with new ideas and a new vision.

Some farmers are dealing with other issues, such as farm succession, or earthquake damage, so you have to acknowledge that probably only ten per cent of the people at any one time are open to change. You just have to keep giving that message. (Marketing people tell us that you have to call someone seven times before the message sinks in.)

It's transformational change we're talking about here – big change. We farmers are human, just like urban people, and slow to change. Why would you start riding your bike when you can still drive your car?

Our obsession with volume is undermining our natural gifts: our water and land sustainability are damaged by overstocking, overuse of nitrogen, and poor management skills.

I've asked nearly every dairy farmer that I've met in the last six months whether they would rather have eight dollars a kilo and halve the volume they produce now, or four dollars a kilo and produce at the current rate of volume. They'd all prefer that first choice, of course. They'd have a better lifestyle and everything would be better for them and better for the environment. But it doesn't happen – because the models are all driven by distributors who want cheap products. The pressure is on to ramp up production and to keep prices down. The directions we get from distributors, and from the people in government who set the terms for our markets, are still all about volume and quantity.

Imagine that you're out for dinner, and the waiter puts a plate of food down in front of you. It looks good – but how good is it really? What is its nutritional content? What's its value in terms of the way it was produced? You pull out your phone, or some kind of mobile scanner, and scan over the plate. The diagnosis pops up on your screen. We're moving fast towards this technology. There will probably be other adaptations, such as a barcode on the menu that you could scan before you order that will tell you all the nutritional and health details of each meal.

Human beings will soon be able to make far more choices about what goes into their bodies. That will benefit producers at the boutique end of production who farm using sustainable processes and natural inputs. That's what needs to be at the leading edge of New Zealand agricultural production. We've got capability in those areas already – not that it shows itself much. In this era, we are swallowed by the volume-and-quantity merchants. And that affects us all.

Let's focus on our natural gifts, and win those premiums.

At Bonavaree today, five-sixths of our farm, at any given time, is now run using only natural nitrogen. Our improved land, the areas with developed lucerne or clovers, gets no nitrogen while it is in production. When the lucerne runs out, we crop that land with green-feed barley, annual ryegrass and rape to use up the nitrogen the lucerne has fixed, and in that phase we also add a little bit of nitrogen, creating ideal conditions for the return of lucerne. We still use a bit of artificial nitrogen strategically on our non-legume crops, but our nitrogen footprint is very, very low.

In terms of nitrogen run-off, our farm now produces six kilograms per hectare per year. Typically, most farms produce between twenty and seventy kilograms per hectare per year, so ours is incredibly low. Our low figure is partly attributable to our dry conditions, but also to our natural nitrogen-fixing capability. To put it further in perspective, the run-off of natural nitrogen from a native forest is three kilograms per hectare per year.

Overall, the sheep and beef sector produces red meat with a low environmental footprint generally. We're not grain feeding, and we're not hormone feeding. We do that pretty well on country that can't do much else.

We are in a great place to fit the future with our systems. But for us to totally remove nitrogen we would need a lot more reward for our product. The only way we have been able to hang in there with greater costs is to get bigger and spread the costs over more animals. So capturing more value is top priority for us, going forward.

I would like to farm without any chemicals, but I don't want to go broke. That's the conundrum.

PART FOUR

28

BECOMING A STRATEGIC FARMER

'Sustainability is not business as usual with a few concessions, but a new road.' —*Dr Morgan Williams, Parliamentary Commissioner for the Environment, in* Growing for Good

I'm embarrassed now at how good I thought I was as a farmer, when in truth there was so much I didn't understand. My successes came by one way alone, and that was working harder. It was only when I was forced to begin challenging my processes with the word 'why' that my eyes began to open.

Until I reached my crisis point it was too difficult for me to see a different way, and it comes down to the fact that I was *in* the fight, not over the fight. I was down there in the engine room. I often think about the Cook Strait ferry, making its way from Wellington towards the Sounds, carrying its passengers across some of the roughest water you'd ever want to be on. What if you were in the lounge eating your dinner when an announcement came from the captain: 'Hold on, ladies and gentlemen, I'm just leaving the bridge and going down to check the dials in the engine room. Let me know if we're suddenly heading off course.' Next minute, you see the captain go running down to the engine room, then a few minutes later you see him rushing somewhere else, still not on the bridge, and the boat starts rolling . . .

That was the sort of ship I was running. I was all over it. I was tearing around the place and getting faster and faster and faster.

When I look back now at my life, I can see that if it hadn't been that drought it would have been something else. That just happened to be the big enough blow. It wasn't a question of whether I was going to prang, but where and when. I was working harder and harder, for less and less return.

At some point during the time I was working alone on the farm, Wendy and I attended a business course in Nelson run by the bank. As preparation we had to write down everything that we'd done in the week before we went there, including what time we went to bed and what time we got up. Were we watching TV in the evenings? What were we doing? We all did this task and handed it in, even though we had no idea how it was going to be used.

We got to the course and the guy who was running it hopped up and said, 'Now I'm going to work out what you're all worth.'

The guy who was worth most was a fellow who owned a company and had 24,000 cows. He hadn't done any hands-on farm work in that past week – he was 100 per cent strategic thinking.

Out of the fourteen people there, guess who was at the other end of the class? Yours truly. Because I was farming on my own, I spent the whole week doing all the farm tasks so I could have this time away, and I spent a lot of time on the tractor. The organiser said: 'Well, Doug, you're the right charlie. All you did was twenty-five-dollars-an-hour work and that's what you're worth. Not much.'

It really helped me realise that I wasn't putting any value into my highest area of influence. I came home from that course quite impressed, but I wasn't yet organised to take advantage of the knowledge. It was only when we began using the Farmax program that I opened up to the possibilities and gained a full appreciation of the values of different levels of work.

Now when I encourage other farmers to take a closer look at the way they work, I talk about the three levels of farming. There's 'work', and I put a rating in New Zealand of $20 to $25 an hour on that. Most farmers are very, very good at work. They can drive tractors, build fences, shift sheep, grub thistles. They can do all this tough, physical stuff. We are a nation of very hard-working farmers.

The problem is, even if you do a sixty-hour week on $20 an hour, it's not much money. If you multiply that by fifty-two you'll see there's no way that business can possibly thrive. And the brutal truth is, there are any number of people who could drive a tractor just as well as you do. I've heard many farmers say, 'I'd like to do feed budgeting or financial planning, but I haven't got time. I'm working sixty hours now. When the hell am I going to bloody well do it?'

The next level of work is tactical work, and it rings in at, say, $100 an hour. That's your feed budgeting, your financial planning and budgeting, and marrying all those together, drawing up the plans for the farm's flow of work. We've got a reasonable number of farmers in New Zealand who are pretty good at that. But if you're doing that sort of work you could probably only do forty hours a week because it's a bit more taxing and you're probably going to have to go to the gym to keep your body functioning right. But forty hours a week times $100 an hour, that's $4000 a week; multiply that by fifty-two and you're beginning to realise a more meaningful situation.

And then above 'work' and 'tactical work' is what I call 'strategic work', which pays, say, $1000 an hour. Some people won't be capable of doing much of that, but a lot are, and that's when you do a systems redesign like we did. People look at me funny when I talk about this and they say: 'I don't think anyone in the rural sector is worth a thousand bucks an hour.'

'Well,' I say, 'I think you're wrong and you're looking at one right now. When I'm in that mode I can show that we've earned lots more than that.'

Our son Fraser spends most of his time in the tactical section now, increasingly moving into the strategic section and very little time in the $25 arena. We can't afford for him to be there; that's what we employ others to do.

In the evenings, watching television with the family, he'll pull out his laptop and do a wee bit of work on Farmax. The other software we use is FarmIQ, which is a mapping program, an event record. We've transformed Bonavaree through our adoption of these powerful technological tools. Fraser had initially been a bit dismissive of my involvement in the SFSCG, but once he met Graeme Ogle he became inspired; soon they were talking a language of their own, and Fraser became completely committed to the process. Ogle one day told me Fraser was the best student Farmax had ever had. Through Fraser and this farm, and others, the two programs have been married together so they talk to each other. I could soon see that there was no way I needed to be doing all this stuff as well as Fraser, so I pulled back and he and Ogle were away. Together, they were a winning formula. Today, Farmax and FarmIQ are used by nearly all of the top percentile of farmers in this country.

Anyway, sitting on the sofa there one night, Fraser ran a few scenarios. We'd planted our autumn crops and it looked as though they

It wasn't a question of whether I was going to prang, but where and when. I was working harder and harder, for less and less return.

were getting off to a good start. 'I'd better just work out how much feed that's going to produce,' he said to himself. We'd done about 300 hectares, so it was quite a big area. He sat down there and tapped away.

The next morning I was sitting in my office. *Knock, knock, knock* on the door. He told me what he'd found.

'If we have an average growth season from now on we will need four hundred more cattle to eat the feed.'

'What? I haven't budgeted for that!'

'Yeah, we need four hundred more cattle. That's if it's average. But Dad, I think that we're actually going to be doing better than average. If we dare to get any rain we might need another couple of hundred on top of that.'

Those animals cost $700–850 apiece, so it's a lot of money. 'Heavens,' I said, 'I'd better ring the bank.'

I rang the bank and got enough money to buy 400 head of cattle; then I rang the dairy agent and he had a client who wanted grazing for 200 dairy cattle, so they joined the ones we bought, and we were making money. How much? We put a conservative estimate of $100,000 on Fraser's two hours of work.

The other guy, the farmer stuck at the 'work' level, would be out crutching sheep or doing whatever he's doing. He'd see his pastures and think, *Those crops are getting away to a good thing*. Then all of a sudden he'd think: *We haven't got enough stock*. But when he goes out to buy the extra stock the price has already gone up, whereas because of our forecasting ability, we got in early before prices rose.

It's all in the foresight and the timing. Two or three weeks after Fraser came knocking at my office door, all the value in that decision had evaporated because the other slow fellows had woken up to the fact it was happening. Game over, finished. They had all gone in and paid top dollar. They'll never retrieve a reward out of it.

I trust science and maths, and our business has been transformed by our adoption of new technologies. If seventy per cent of farmers using these powerful software packages are better off, then that's compelling. Yet some farmers say to me, oh yeah, I tried it but it's not for me; or, it's not quite perfect so I don't want to use it.

The power we've gained from learning to use this software is immense. It's not perfect, but I know our investment in it has helped us make rapid progress and growth. And isn't it always the case with new things that you have to *start* in order to get the reward; and the start is the lowest reward? It's the hardest part. Reward builds with time. I understand that everything I engage in that's worthwhile will have patches that are hard. The reward doesn't come first; it comes second – in farming as in life.

Thanks to the software, we are driven now by knowledge, and it has transformed our business.

We used to carry 100 per cent capital stock – that is, our stock stayed on the farm with us through all of the breeding and growth cycle. We did virtually no trading of animals. Today our business is fifty per cent breeding – we love seeing the elevated process of genetic improvement – and the other half is what we call 'opportunity stock'. We don't even call it trading any more, because 'trading stock' doesn't describe what we're trying to do. We shift animals onto and off the farm as we manage our volatile supply-and-demand curve for feed.

We make sure nothing we do creates work without also creating value. A herb farmer I met in Australia recently told me he won't plant until he has a fair return signed up. Maybe next year I won't put the ram out until we have a high-price contract.

We've been recording our data for so long now that we know exactly what growth rates we will get from a known quality of feed. Calves might be growing at a rate of 75 grams to one kilogram a day

– so we can ask ourselves, if we take them to this point here, what's the sale price likely to be? Fraser will tap into Farmax and ensure we're getting optimum returns. It's upper-level thinking as opposed to being out driving the tractor.

The old Doug Avery used to buy and sell stock, but I pretty much always thought that if I bought some cattle I really had to finish them, and I'd only sell them in a crisis. But Fraser Avery, he looks at his process all the time. He'll think, *Gee, I've got 250 yearling bulls here and that spot price at the moment for them is just unbelievable; $4.30, let's just take it.* We've got them off the farm and don't have to worry about them when the sun comes out and things get really dry. We'll bring some animals back a few months later – maybe even the same ones – because we've got feed saved and then we can bring them down to the lucerne and accelerate the growth and still get to the finishing point at the same time.

The moral of the story is that we've moved away from confronting nature. In the old days I was always facing nature head-on. There was the environment and the challenge, and the farmer who was running it – me – was too thick to work it out. But part of the reason I was too thick is I didn't have time. I was running myself ragged with my $25 an hour physical pace, and I couldn't afford to lift my eyes to see the bigger picture.

We need to be more smart. Lift your eyes. We're still educating people for an industrial era but we don't have an industrial era any more; this is the knowledge era.

Since the beginning of the SFSCG our farm has gone from a $350,000 a year enterprise a multi-million-dollar business. This is the fruit we are picking.

29

DRAFTING GATE IN THE BRAIN

If a man sees the world the same at fifty that he saw at twenty, he's wasted thirty years of his life.

Wendy and I got to fifty and I said to her, I just love travel. Prior to that we'd hardly taken any holidays. We were a chip off the old model – that's the one where the farmer has built up this massive asset but has learned to be really stingy with himself. But by then, I was coming right in my head, the farm was going well and we had Fraser, who'd come back in 2002 and was on a path to take over.

Wendy and I started talking and we got really excited. Wouldn't it be great if we travelled each year? We made a pledge to do just that. Far out, why didn't we start that earlier in life?

It all became so exciting. Every trip we did drew us closer to what we loved. We've been through Malaysia. We've been to Bali, Vietnam, Thailand, China and Cambodia.

We travelled in Asia because it was easy for us and it was cheap. We just loved the cut and thrust of Asia, the business and the excitement and the bizarre. We've seen Peru and Uruguay and now a little bit of Canada and a little of Alaska. Turkey and Greece, too, plus a quick look-in at Africa. We've been pretty much all over Australia.

Wendy and I did go to Cairns one time when we were younger, although we were comparatively old, and I looked at all these kids out touring and travelling and I felt envious.

Now I understand that if you feel envious you've got a problem, so you've got to fix something and get rid of the envy; because while you're envious about anything you just won't make good calls.

All that stuff multiplies. Even the slightest negative thought can eat away at you and debilitate you. Envy and regret: I believe those feelings, if left unchecked, will rot you from the inside out.

The key, in my view, is to manage what goes into your head. *I've just heard this information and it's really bad.* Park it in a safe place while you give yourself a chance to make a considered emotional response, rather than just whacking it straight back. When my negative thoughts come in, they go into my processing unit. The amygdala is the technical term. I like calling it the grumpy zone because that's easy for me. That grumpy zone is like a drafting gate for a sheep race. You have a choice about where you send that thought: you can let it go to the back, and if it goes to the back you're in trouble because that'll take you down.

I also like to think of this process in terms of gardening. You can grow weeds or vegetables in a garden, and the top vegetable gardeners fertilise their positive thoughts and grow great vegetables. But if you take in rubbish and you let that rubbish multiply, you don't get the crop you want.

Our brain is so much like a vegetable garden. Managing our thoughts is a cultivated process; it's a learned management business. You get feelings and thoughts, they turn into words, and those words turn into behaviours. Everybody else in your life is judging you by what comes out of you in that situation. If you are using ugly words, you will chase away beautiful people and be attractive to uglier people. It just multiplies itself up. That's life.

This stuff isn't just important; it's bloody important. Life's tough; deal with it. But make *choices* in how to deal with it.

The best way for me to deal with those feelings, if I start to detect them, is to get on with something that's going to make me feel excited. It might be a project or something. I like projects. I love projects! I'm no longer fearful about stuff. I used to go, oh, what happens if that goes wrong? Now I think to myself, well, what happens if it goes right? And all my energy goes to ensuring that I put my energies into the influences that will make it go right. It can't go right if it's not tried. It's a positive mindset. As human beings we're naturally embedded in the 'what if it goes wrong?' thought processes. I'm so glad I now recognise and manage that in myself.

Our younger son Richard, the ultrarunner, spoke to the Platinum Primary Producers conference in 2017 about how he meets the challenge of covering those massive distances. I was blown away by what he said. Failure, he said, means attempt number one . . . and if it's going to be a challenge, often the chance of failure must be high. Make the choice to give up choice; never quit unless you should quit.

So now, instead of feeling envy and regret, we travel a lot, often as part of my attendance at conferences, and the world has opened out to us and we get all these new influences on our thinking and our awareness.

Soon after my Beyond Reasonable Drought speaking tour (see chapter 30), I was invited by Suncorp Bank to do an Australian tour. Queensland was in the grip of a terrible drought, far worse than

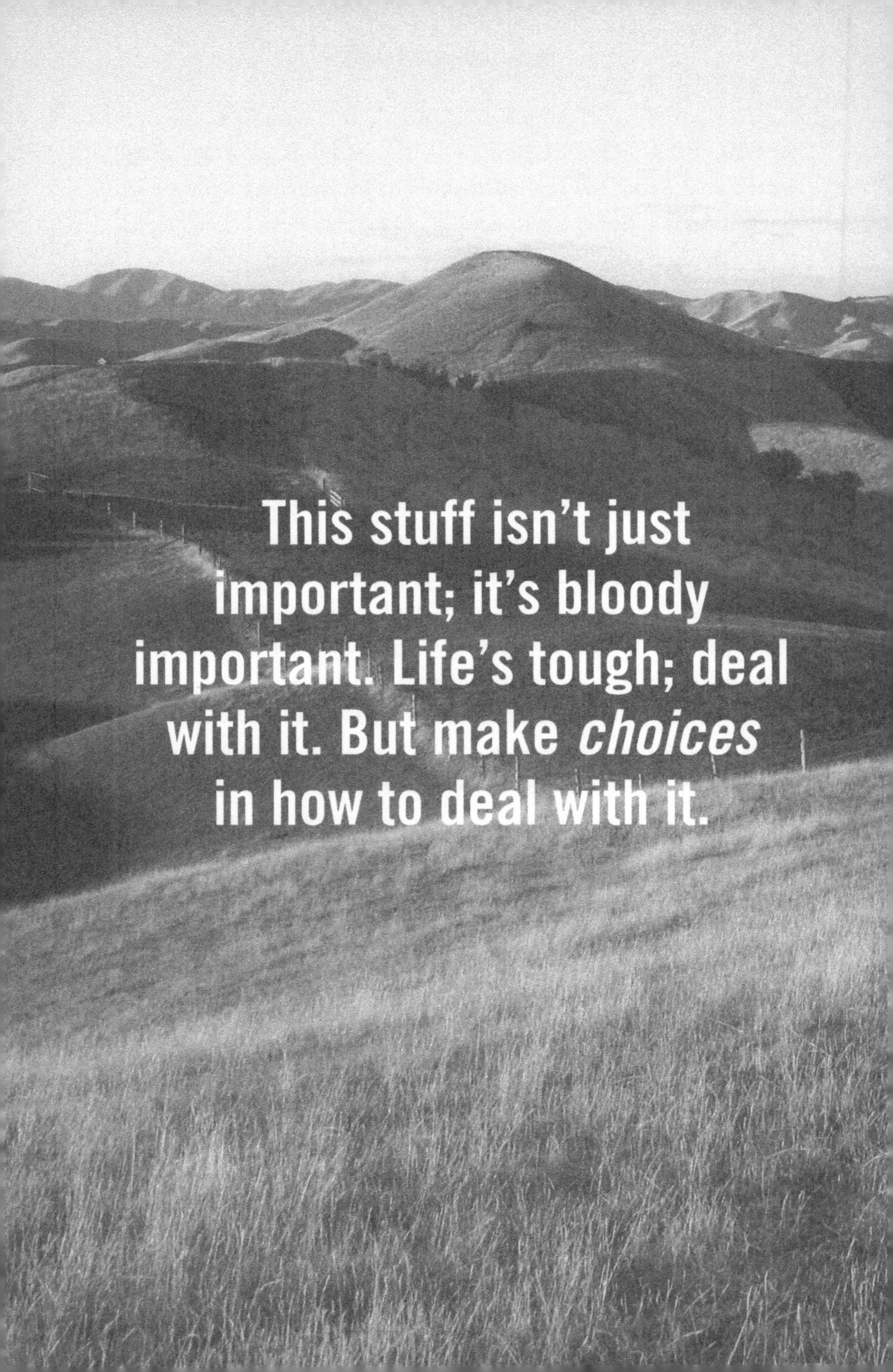

This stuff isn't just important; it's bloody important. Life's tough; deal with it. But make *choices* in how to deal with it.

anything I've been in, and they asked me to share my story. They teamed me up with psychologist Dennis Hoiberg, a specialist in change management and emotional resilience.

In our first event, Hoiberg spoke before me. Dennis has been described as a psychologist on steroids, and I was riveted as I watched him take charge of the crowd with his brutal Aussie voice and his self-deprecating humour. Bouncing forward, resilience . . . it was Dennis who really brought those words to life, not just for me, but to the stressed, exhausted people in the audience. It was all the stuff I'm most passionate about, but he added the fancy words to explain what was going on in our heads. It was he who introduced me to the amygdala (which, in case you don't know, is the bit of the brain responsible for our emotional responses) and to serotonin, a chemical in our body that is believed to be responsible for maintaining mood balance.

How, I wondered, would I follow him? I had to shake myself to remember that I was on next and to get ready. *Doug! Stop listening and prepare your own process!*

For that whole tour, I was sponge-learning, and with his blessing I've incorporated much of his knowledge and messaging into my own presentations.

Those Australian audiences . . . That tour taught me that for everything we think is tough, they have it tougher, often by multiple degrees, and I think that's why I came to love those people from the outback so much. They have a dry sense of humour, and they need every bit of it at times to keep their balance. We spoke in Miles, in St George, then Roma. And it was there that a man stood up to ask a question. 'Doug,' he said, 'I loved your speech. You talked about resilience, but what if you owned a farm where the least depth of water was one metre?' His wife, he told the crowd, had been rescued by helicopter following a severe flood, and as she was airlifted to safety, they flew across 100 kilometres of flooded landscape.

Obviously I can't solve that for him, or make that disaster any less. The scale of what some people are up against is absolutely terrifying – as it was for the farmers and other people of Ward and Kaikoura during and after the massive earthquakes of 2013 and 2016.

Even in the greatest disaster, the choice is stark: you learn or you lose. The dice have rolled, but life goes on. On my journey, I've learned that everything that's bad has always got something good attached to it. As human beings we tend to focus in times of adversity on what's gone wrong rather than what's right. Everything – *everything* – has a teaching component, a learning element. If you don't learn, you lose. It only becomes failure if you don't learn. With this thinking there are only two possible results: either you win or you learn. This thinking pattern helps me a lot in managing my difficult times.

I've seen many farmers build up a chip on their shoulder about how well other people live in comparison with them. We tend to have a high value asset, but a comparatively low return. And we have one other thing that saves the industry from going bankrupt. Like most farmers, I run two businesses here: I've got a business that produces animal meat, wool and seed production, and I've got a land-holding business. It's just the same situation as urban people, with their house ownership.

I've worked really hard all my life, even if sometimes it's not been very well directed. But in the primary business of farming I've really only ever just made a living and never had spare cash; everything has been ground into the business. All the time I was running that business, though, my land investment business has boomed. And on some of those days when I was in total despair, the new valuations would come, three years since the last one, and I'd sit down and divide the capital gain on paper by the amount of hours that I'd worked, and I'd find enough reward in that to keep going. It's a tax-free reward, but of course we never cash it in.

But the old cocky with his farm: he's been stingy all his life. He's got a good truck, but the house is a shambles, the kitchen's never been done up, and he's got a big chip on his shoulder towards the people he hears about who get $100,000 a year, rain or shine. The farm might have gone up a million dollars in the last valuation; he doesn't work that out until he sells, and so he postpones all of life's pleasures till that day. He buys his ticket for Europe to see the All Blacks, which is what he's wanted to do all of his life, and that's when the doctor says, 'No, your heart's no good.' Then he goes back down to the bank and puts the money back and says, 'Geez, I can't go.' His chin goes down, and then he dies. That's what happens; I see it all the time.

In this modern generation of farmers, the wives say, 'I haven't had my kitchen done up for ten years. It's getting done up. I just looked at our valuation the other day and the valuation has gone up two hundred thousand, so I want a new kitchen or else I'm out.'

'Okay, darling, I'll get you a new kitchen.'

So there's a major change. The young guys are saying, *Everybody else that's got a job, they actually take three weeks' holiday a year. Mum and Dad didn't and look how bitter they turned out to be.* We've got a revolution occurring and that new group of farmers will be a whole lot better off because they'll choose to live a more normal life. They won't leave it too late to reap the rewards of their life's labour.

30

NATURAL-BORN ENTREPRENEUR

I tried to be normal once . . . but it was the worst two minutes of my life.

With some people, their expectations run to the meat raffle at the pub on Friday night and they can do that for forty years and be happy. I really admire those people if that's what makes them tick. I've never felt like that; for me, there is no end. There won't be a time when I think, oh, that's enough, I can just sit back and do nothing. I get really bored when nothing's happening. A person like me thinks, *Things are going quite good – so what can we do next?*

You can't make an entrepreneur; you're either born that way or you're not. Entrepreneurs are a tiny group of people in the population. They get a lot wrong, they go broke, they take enormous risks that other people would never dare to take. But they get some stuff – some immense stuff – right.

Adrenaline is everything. I sometimes think it would be nice to simply be content, and then I think, hell, I can't imagine how bad that must be. I believe we can all moderate ourselves, we can change aspects of our behaviour and attitudes, but we can't change people completely. This thing that's in me, the thing that can't sit still and that always needs to go on pushing: it's fundamental and unchangeable. The period of my life when I stagnated was the worst time of my life. It almost killed me. And part of the problem was that I didn't have the language or self-knowledge to understand the kind of person I was, nor what my problems were really all about.

A lot of people will look at a deal and they'll think, the lights aren't all green so I won't do it. Those people would make good lawyers because lawyers are good at mitigating all risk. But good businesspeople know that you can't mitigate all risk; in fact we have a great capacity to take on acceptable risk.

If you haven't got that capacity, don't go into business because actually it's so hard out there you'll do yourself damage. A good businessperson accepts risk, mitigates against it, and builds it into their equation. We know what we are prepared to lose; we fix our eye on what we can win. That's solution thinking again.

That's the way I approach agriculture. What's our best way to mitigate the risk? It's to get the production cycles working properly, to achieve maximum utilisation of water, and to put systems in place where we can be in or out of farming quickly.

Progressively as a family, especially over the last fifteen years, we've built up so much knowledge about managing this challenging country. Bonavaree has continued to grow. My grandparents set out in 1919 with 206 hectares. Since then Wendy and I have acquired six further blocks, the most recent in March 2016. Bonavaree now comprises 2034 hectares, or 2400 hectares including two blocks that we lease.

This isn't size for size's sake. We have expanded because of the accelerated value we know we can achieve with each purchase, and that's what drives me forward as an entrepreneur. It's no use going and buying the next-door neighbour's property if you're not going to create any more value. All great plans have to have an accelerated value-creation component in there somewhere.

Acceleration; I'm lost without it.

The three years of the SFSCG were non-stop excitement and learning on the farm, but something else happened, too. As our project went on and people became aware something different was happening, I began to be asked all over the place to talk to other rural people about what we were doing. I was engaging with the community in ways I never had before – and I loved it.

A real excitement built around the SFSCG and, as we came to a close, the whole process culminated with a field day – we called it Beyond Reasonable Drought – at Bonavaree. It was the chance for our science professionals to step forward. As the day grew nearer it became apparent this wasn't going to be any ordinary field day.

I rang OSH. 'We've got a field day on here tomorrow. We thought we might get a hundred to a hundred and fifty people, and I've been told it could be over four hundred. What happens if there's an accident?'

'It will all be your responsibility,' they said.

Farmers came from as far south as Dipton and from as far north as Wairoa and Gisborne. Some stayed in Kaikoura, and one of the hotels put on a champagne breakfast for them. Boffins came from Wellington. In the end, 420 people converged on this place.

It was the most stressful day of my life. I got up at five o'clock in the morning and I knew that everything was going to be stretched; even the toilets were going to be taxed. We had big urns that we needed to begin heating up so we could make cups of tea. I switched one on and its light went on, and then I switched another on and blew all the circuitry.

I raced home, couldn't find any fuse wire, so went to my neighbours, and woke him up at half past five. *Do you have any fuse wire?*

We fixed it up but it blew again just as the first PowerPoint was about to be given. By the time I'd fixed it again our marquee had so many people in it that some were nearly flaking with the heat. We had got the biggest marquee in the upper South Island and it was chocker. So I took my knife out and I ripped it down the side, cutting the ropes and throwing the walls open. I thought, *Oh my God, I'm not going to make it through the day.*

We had so many four-wheel drives taking people around the farm that by the time one lot were exiting a block, the other lot were still going in. A cavalcade of vehicles snaked its way through our land.

For a few days afterwards, Fraser and I were so blown out we couldn't remember where our stock were on the farm. I don't think there was a time before or since when we wouldn't have known exactly where every one was. We had a bit of a debrief next morning and Fraser said, 'I can't even think where we are.'

'I'm the same,' I said.

People talked for ages about that day. I got letters and emails and phone calls for months. And then, all of a sudden, I felt lost. *This is all finished; it's all over.* There was a big vacuum. The farm was going really well and I was involved but Fraser was quietly moving his shoulder further down under a lower rib, just edging me out, which I accepted as being healthy.

I guess you could say it was business as usual. I dreadfully missed the pressure of engagement, the acid that had been put on us during the SFSCG. Then one day, must have been mid-2010, I spotted this little ad: South Island Farmer of the Year. And I thought, *Bugger it, I'll have a go.*

A good businessperson accepts risk, mitigates against it, and builds it into their equation. We know what we are prepared to lose; we fix our eye on what we can win. That's solution thinking again.

I love reward. The changes that we've made to our business have brought growth and profit, strengthening each of the legs – financial, environmental, social – of the stool. Those are internal rewards. But, like most people, external reward is important to me: recognition from my peers that my work is valuable.

Soon after the SFSCG ended, the Landcare Trust entered the project into the Ministry for the Environment's Green Ribbon Awards and we won the sustainable land use category.

Mostly, I thought entering Farmer of the Year would be a good thing to get me busy, and put a bit of pressure on myself again to examine where we'd got to. I wanted the development that comes with being scrutinised. And some people would say I wasn't in front of enough lights and mirrors, and that's probably another way of looking at it. I'd come to very much enjoy being engaged with so many people.

When people came to our place for that field day in 2008 and saw what we'd achieved since 2004, they thought it was amazing. But by the time I entered the Farmer of the Year our output had doubled again.

The judges came for the first time and we hopped in the truck and I showed them around the farm. They grew quieter and quieter. Then we came back and sat around the table and had a bit of a chat. The questioning was tough. Then they came back a second time and drilled me again. I was overwhelmed with a sense of everything we weren't doing. There was a new judge, Barry Brook, former chief executive of PGG Wrightson and chairman of Synlait Farms, and he started to drill down into the fact that we had massive gaps in our strategic thinking and didn't have processes for approaching the farm in a strategic way. That's when I thought, *Far out, in the endeavour to win the Farmer of the Year I can see it going out the door with their briefcases when they leave.*

'I'm so sorry,' I said to everyone once the judges had gone, 'I think that was a waste of time. We've been opened like a can of worms.'

Then we went down to the finals at Lincoln University. Among the other finalists were Craige and Roz Mackenzie, and we got chatting.

They'd developed a new system for precision application of water, nutrients and pesticides, allowing much lower applications of these, and less run-off. It was obvious to me their achievement was great, and in fact they've since won the national Farm Environment Award. *Oh, gee, it'll be a long day at the office tonight.* I was sure I had no chance against them.

The judges awarded the fourth place, then the third, and that wasn't us. Then second place was announced and that was . . . the Mackenzies. And I knew. 'Yes!' And sure enough, South Island Farmer of the Year was the Avery family – me, Wendy, Fraser, and his wife Shelley.

Later, when I was talking to one of the judges, I asked why they'd been so quiet that first day they came to look around the farm.

'The day that we came to your farm on the first occasion, we met at Christchurch Airport and we were all having a bit of a giggle. We were going up to Marlborough to waste a day. Honestly we weren't overly bloody excited about that day,' he confessed.

'Yeah, we went quiet all right. You blew the socks off us all. We had no idea that there was farming at the level you guys are doing in that area. We all know how tough it is. We've all been through our own drought. We went into your place and at the time that district was really dry. Your place looked so amazing, your stock was so amazing, your figures were so amazing. That's when you won it. You won it the first bloody day. We were gobsmacked.'

Soon after that, we won the Marlborough Environment Award. Those awards ramped me up. They gave me confidence, and opportunities to tell our story. I was off again, like a dog with a bone.

I did a speaking tour, that (of course) I called Beyond Reasonable Drought, to eight venues on the east coast, and the response was incredible. In Gisborne, some 300 people packed into the Emerald Hotel. People were telling me they felt inspired and they wanted to change their lives. What surprised me was that it wasn't just the lucerne they were interested in. They wanted somebody to help them think a different way.

I didn't really understand that aspect at first. Back then, I didn't talk much about my personal story of depression and how bad that all got. I just focused on the work we'd done with Derrick Moot and the SFSCG scientists. I wasn't yet aware of the scale of need in the rural community for a message of help and resilience.

But every time I spoke, the response was extraordinary – and it made me feel good. It's very nice to feel that your efforts are appreciated and valued. I was getting my feeling of value back, and it was like petrol in an engine, my foot flat on the pedal. That's such a rollover for a man who felt he had no value to give. It was a thousand-mile trek in just a few years. It's been a strange old journey.

31

THE GOLDEN AGE FOR AGRICULTURE

Farming is not about Trev, that classic stereotype of a farmer dancing around in the paddock with gumboots and a black singlet on. He's out of his depth in the new world of farming.

When I was at the Platinum Primary Producers conference in Melbourne in early 2017 I met an extraordinary man, a herb farmer. Jan Vydra established his hydroponic herb business, Australian Fresh Leaf Herbs, nine years ago and employs eighty-five people on his two state-of-the-art greenhouse farms. He loves plants, but his business partner is a banker. He told me he doesn't see himself as a farmer. 'I'm a logistics operator,' he told me. And I thought, 'So am I!'

Jan spends his days organising tracks and pathways for nutrients and water, taking care of the business of demand and supply – and he's in the middle of it all, pulling stuff together. In the same way, Fraser now is not really a farmer – he operates a farm, but he's operating all day on the flow of communications and transactions. He earns what's probably a higher salary than a headmaster of a reasonably sized school, and his responsibilities would be as great.

We employ other guys to actually farm. Our young stock manager is already on a very good salary, with a ute and a paid education path and so on. Free meat, of course. By the time he leaves here, which he invariably will because he'll outgrow this position, he'll be qualified for a standalone manager's job and attract anything from $100,000 to $120,000, which out in rural New Zealand is a good salary.

The capital employed in Bonavaree is now in the millions, so it's a hell of a lot of money. It's a hell of a lot of debt. If you see the BNZ go past let me know, will you? I'll go and hide in the bedroom! But you can't really have a clown in charge, and there are no clowns around here. It's a really serious business out there at any given time.

I talk all the time now about 'why'. That question is the centre of our universe. Generation Y is also the centre of our universe. Look around our farm: Generation Y is running it, not Generation Baby Boomer. They've got their cell phones and they're plugging all their paddock data into the central computer system and onto the Cloud.

I did a tour organised by Rural Women; I was their poster boy for the International Year of the Farming Family. I did my best to celebrate that – we are a farming family here, after all – but I'm not sure that model will endure into the future. This farm is an example of how sophisticated things are, and of the skill set that goes with the complete range of work here.

So many of our farming businesses are failing because there's the expectation that it's got to be a family farm. Kids, the next generation, get passed a poisoned chalice. They're farming people because that's the lifestyle they're familiar with, but for the kind of farming that's required today, a lot of them lack the physical or mental attributes.

We see images on TV of farmers who clearly aren't coping – their farms aren't well cared for, their animals are not at peak. They're run ragged. Some of those guys went into farming with no idea of the sort of work they're now being asked to do. They wouldn't know how to do it or where to begin. To be honest, there's not a lot of people with the right attributes lining up to do the work because it's seen as such a bloody tough existence, and it's getting tougher by the day.

Part of the problem is the way farmers see themselves. As I've explained, being a farmer is not about grunt labour – low-value work, long hours and drudgery – but about strategic thinking. If we could move farmers away from spending all their time in the cowshed to developing a more critical sense of the value of their lives, we could get the industry onto a smarter, more sustainable footing.

I'm one of the Ministry for Primary Industries' Champions of Agriculture – a campaign to make this industry look more appealing to young people. We won't solve the problems in farming until we get people of the right calibre. In the food production industry we don't get our share of the high-fliers.

Some people think that by fixing the bottom you lift the top, but I don't think it works that way. The top pulls the bottom up – and we need more people. In the words of my friend Shane McManaway, the CEO of Allflex Australasia and a Wairarapa farmer, this is the golden age for careers in agriculture.

In 2010, Landcorp and Silver Fern Farms asked me to chair a sequence of seminars around the country to launch the FarmIQ computer program. It was a chance to talk to farmers about change. 'I'd love to do that,' I said.

The first meeting was in Dargaville and it was the worst day of my life, I reckon, as I've never struck such a negative group of people. There were about four old farmers in there and everything that we put forward – *nah*, they had something go wrong twenty years ago and they kept turning us back to that.

'We're here to try to bloody well break the cycle that we're in, a cycle of failure in the sheep industry,' I told them. 'These new initiatives will see a much better relationship between consumers and us as producers.'

Nothing worked. They were nothing but naughty old boys all day. I limped through the full six hours of the seminar. My sister, who lives in Dargaville, came down to watch and she said, 'Oh my God, Doug, I'm so embarrassed. I didn't realise we had such negative old bastards in the community.' I said, 'Well you have.' I thought, *I've got nine more of these to go.*

The next day we ran exactly the same seminar at a rugby club near Te Awamutu. The first person who came through the door was under seventy and I thought, *Far out, today might be a bit different.* A couple arrived and they said, 'We've got our kids with us, is that okay?' I said, 'Come in, come in. Take a seat. I don't care if they cause mayhem all day.'

The day was completely different. Exactly the same delivery, completely different people. At the end of the day I hopped up and I said, 'You've been such a wonderful group of people, I'd like to sing you a song.'

They were all looking at me thinking, *What is he going to do now?*

It's a bit of a naughty song but it takes a nice swing at hard times, and people love it.

There's always someone worse off than you,
If you stop and think about it you know it's true,
Look on the bright side or in reverse,
It can only get better, can't get any worse

She came home from work wearing a smile,
She said, I'm pregnant love, you'll be a dad in a while,

He said, We can't afford a baby, and really went berserk,
She said, Don't worry, I'm on compo . . . it happened at work.

The whole place just erupted into laughter. Humans suck up the tough stuff better if they are travelling in a light mode. From then on I've always sung. I get the crowds to sing the chorus, threatening to go home if they don't join in, and if they do I sing another verse.

Eventually the day was over. It had been so much fun. We did the same thing in Gisborne, and at the end of that meeting one of the attendees, an Allflex rep called Mark McManaway raced to call his brother Shane on the phone.

'What are you doing tomorrow?'

'I've got a bit on,' he said.

'No,' Mark told him, 'cancel that. Go to Dannevirke. There's this crazy bastard coming through and you'll never have more fun in your life.'

Shane thought, well, his brother had never rung him up like that before; better do it.

About eighty or ninety farmers turned up in Dannevirke, some of them staunch landholders of massive proportion. Like me, they've found the last twenty years tough. But they became hugely engaged in the presentations as the day went by, and when I got to the end of the day and I sang to them, they all joined in and the whole room went crazy. The courage to be wacky has given me some great days.

Shane McManaway came up to me afterwards and introduced himself as the CEO of Allflex Australasia, and also the chair of the Platinum Primary Producers Group, a network of agriculture industry movers and shakers. 'I want you to speak at our conference,' he said. 'I've got the prime minister coming along and you can choose whether you speak before him or after him.'

That was the start of a relationship that changed my life. I call

Shane my enabler, as he took me on to another stage of the journey. I did indeed speak at the PPP conference in March 2011 – although the prime minister was substituted by his then deputy, Bill English – and I met inspiring people by the dozen, and all of that shaped the thinking I have today. I was invited to join the group, and now many of my speaking engagements and fruitful relationships come from that association.

One of the many great things the PPP does is it offers the Zanda McDonald Award, open to people working in the agriculture sector who are aged thirty-five and under. It highlights the very cream of our crop and allows them to flourish. They're the next generation; our industry succession plan; the smart ones who will change our world. The inaugural winner in 2015 was twenty-seven-year-old Emma Hegarty, a beef extension officer for Queensland's Department of Agriculture and Fisheries.

Emma got in touch in early 2017, upset that she couldn't come to that year's PPP conference, as she was pregnant. 'Look at these,' she messaged me, sending through some moving images of her foetus, and also of her tummy going up and down with a basketball game going on inside.

So when I got to my feet at the end of the conference to give my speech, I told everyone that story. 'I've seen the next generation,' I said. 'What we've created here is an incubator of excellence. How many people in this room aren't feeling excited about where we're going in this movement and what can unroll from here?

So you can see what I mean about Trev. He just doesn't fit in this context of solution-seekers, where knowledge and capability are the name of the game. But the only way I'll ever be right about that is if, as a country, we turn our energy to solutions rather than abuse and blame.

32

CLOSING THE GAP

Some years ago, the principal of Seddon Primary School told me one day that he'd decided to cancel the annual school garden competition.

'There are no entries,' he said.

'There's one.'

'There's your son,' he admitted, 'but there's no one else.'

'I'd like you to revisit the decision,' I said.

'It's a waste of time. He's going to get first.'

We managed to find some more kids to enter and the competition went ahead. I was relieved, as Wendy and I always encouraged our children to have gardens and to love gardening. Any produce that came from their garden they got supermarket value for when it was put on the table. If they produced a lettuce and a lettuce was selling for 50 cents they got 50 cents.

It brought up some magical discussions. We'd be in the supermarket and the kids would be saying, 'Dad, you ripped me off the other day.

Lettuces are bringing sixty cents. You only gave me fifty-five.' People would look at me as if they were thinking, *Goodness me, what horrible parents, expecting their children to furbish the table.*

The neat part about that was what it did for our children. As well as teaching them to be gardeners, it taught them about contribution and it taught them about value. They all grew up with a very keen sense of how hard it is to make a dollar.

A few years later I watched a community garden developing in Mangere and they were saying how they had these kids from dysfunctional backgrounds all down there working in the garden and they were seeing immediate changes in their behaviour. That's because they got their hands in the dirt. They plugged back into where they came from. It's why any of us are here, actually. When we garden, we complete the cycle.

I have always dreamed that I could close the knowledge gap between urban and rural folk. But the gap is widening. Seldom before in history have people been so separate from the means of food production.

Urban people condemn farmers for wrecking the environment and treating their animals badly; rural people are frustrated that urban people sit in judgement without helping them find solutions, and that they overlook how hard farmers themselves are working to find solutions.

Of course it's right that people should have a concern about the humane treatment of animals, and nobody I have any respect for in agriculture is not in that process. My default position on that is, I think I have the moral and spiritual right to humbly produce and utilise food accurately and non-wastefully. When I see fish being dumped at sea and any kind of shocking waste of life, that bloody tears me to bits.

On this farm at odd times events occur that I just wish like hell we'd never been involved in – the sheep dying on the lucerne is an example. But that's also true with the motorway. Stuff happens, and we learn from it.

At the end of the day, our world – our human, heavily populated world – still requires organised food production and collection. We need to ask the right question: what do people want? If you start off by asking people what they want, most people want the same thing. They want safe food and clean rivers, and land that can be used over and over again. Those are good starting points for a discussion – our points of agreement. Yet we tend to define ourselves by the things that we don't like rather than the things that we do.

One thing I know for sure. Yelling abuse will never bring a solution. It lets us know there's a problem . . . but provide a solution? Never.

Urban or rural, we are part of nature, part of the planet's processes. I love the visionary thinking about vertical farms in cities – high-rises that are agricultural production centres with a fish farm in the basement, the fish effluent contributing to the fertility of the balcony gardens. If we could grab hold of those ideas, one thing will lead to another: more urban people could become gardeners; and when people put their hands into soil it's like plugging in to the mains.

They don't care how much we know until they know how much we care. At Bonavaree we are visitor-ready 365 days a year. We have had many hundreds of visitors here in the last ten years. We have an open-gate policy, and we invite people to come and get alongside us and understand what we're doing. We're very open. There are no secrets here.

I urge farmers to take down their *Trespassers will be prosecuted* signs and set up a BMX track or a walking track or a hiking track, because the biggest problem we have is most people don't understand the challenges we have as business operators.

Farmers live on the land. They love their land and most are environmentalists at heart. I've yet to meet anyone who deliberately causes damage to the environment. Are there better ways that some of us could be farming? Yes. But we need to make a living and we've been trained a certain way.

I'd like to turn the debate around to ask, how can we all add to the value of this thing? The value input, in my view, of somebody who's concerned about the environment is to help in the solution process. That's the real value entry point.

All sorts of changes are coming. We will find ways galore of growing food in the heart of our cities. That's exciting. But there will still be a role for farmers as managers of the land and producers of wealth.

For urban people, the challenge – as it is for rural people, too – is to move from their circle of concern to their circle of influence. When people focus on opportunity and result, they, like the geese, start to form into the power groups to create that change. That's when human beings are at their most awesome, and that will help to drive change in the way that we farm.

As I've reached out into the community, greater horizons have started to appear for me, bringing new opportunities. Travelling overseas, representing New Zealand at conferences and viewing farms in a number of different countries have all been very powerful experiences. Everywhere, the red carpet has been laid out for me as a New Zealand farmer. I hadn't realised how highly we New Zealand farmers are respected for our efficiency, our technological know-how, our superb ability to produce food.

Travel has made me so grateful for the gifts we have in New

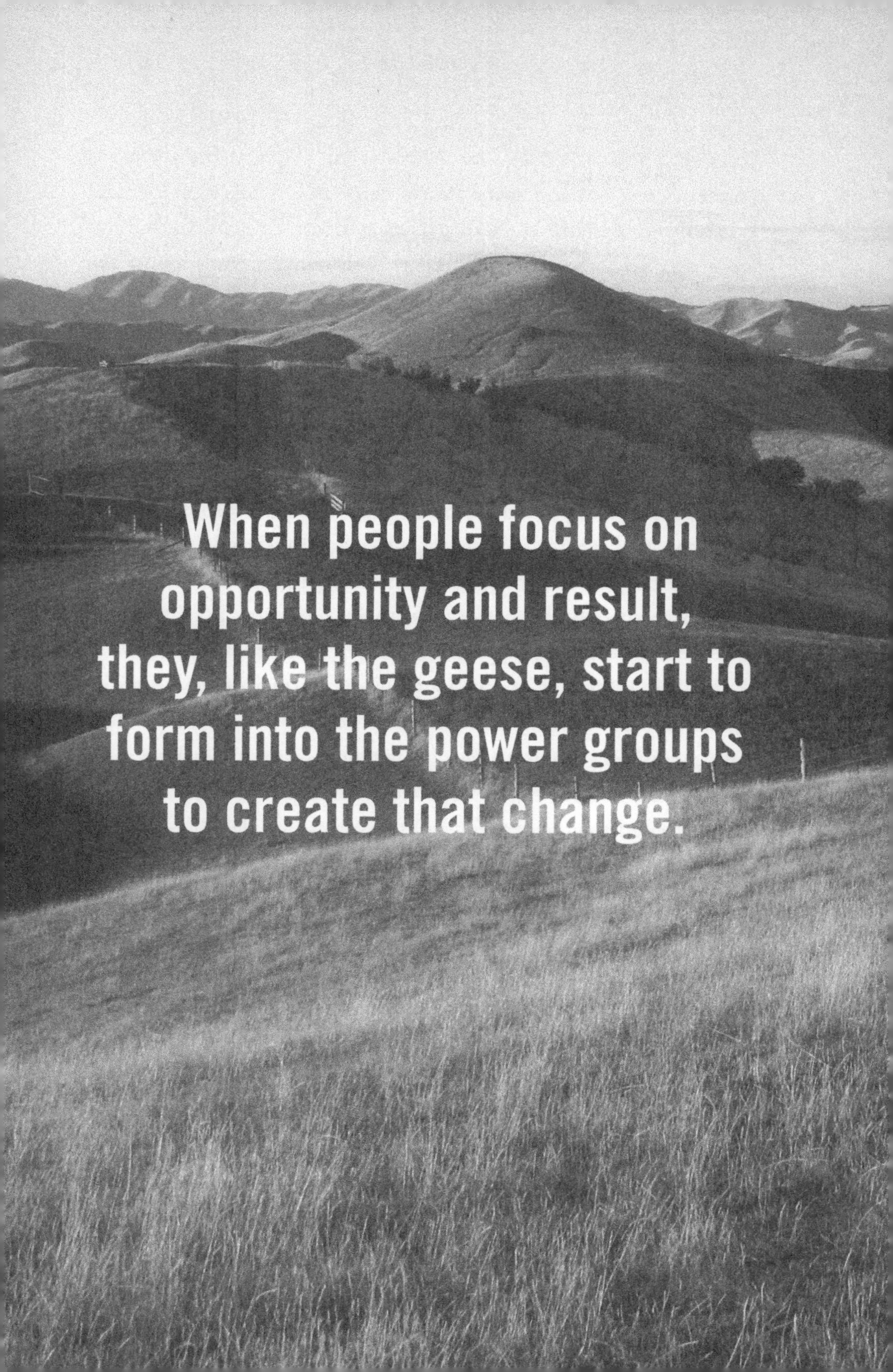

When people focus on opportunity and result, they, like the geese, start to form into the power groups to create that change.

Zealand. I was asked by our Ministry of Primary Industries to represent New Zealand at the World Farmers' Organisation General Assembly in Zambia in 2016. Africa is home to sixty-six million farmers, and I learned how different their conversations are to the ones we have in New Zealand. There, conversation focuses on food security: what are we going to eat; how are we going to get it; how do we make sure people don't starve? I realised few people live in a world like ours that has never been short of food, and I was humbled to be one of only about 36,000 farmers in New Zealand. *Give us our daily bread* . . . what a difference in perception and emphasis.

Tensions are high at the moment between rural people and the rest of the New Zealand electorate, but my main learning from travel is how important relationships are between farmers, urban people and political people, no matter what their persuasion. It's fatal when key elements of an economy stop talking to each other.

In 2011, as a result of our South Island Farmer of the Year win, we travelled to Uruguay via Peru. We were hosted by Silver Fern Farms, who were looking at a joint venture with a Uruguayan meat company. Silver Fern Farms supplied a driver and translator for us, and we toured the country for eight days, visiting dairy, beef, sheep and even rice farms. I got such a great insight into how Uruguay works as a country, and that in turn fed into some great insights to our own situation.

My mouth hung open at the untaken opportunities I saw in Uruguay. And I came to realise that they are bogged down by their political system and heritage. Historically, land was used as a reward to military generals, and life was so easy for them, they had no need of innovation. The rich land-owning class live in Montevideo or large cities. They visit their farms as country retreats, and the wonderful houses are kept especially for these visits. They have little incentive to drive major growth. Farm management is done by gauchos who are paid little and, as a result, do little. Rural education and services are so poor that anyone with the means or the drive to do so moves to live in the cities.

The people who have the enthusiasm and energy to create change and progress have no access to capital; they can never go to a bank and get help meeting their dream, and never will have in their current system. Like the flea in the bowl, they have given up jumping.

I returned to South America in 2015 when I was selected as one of two New Zealand representatives for a Global Research Alliance study tour to Argentina. Part one of this trip was to Palmerston North to learn about the science work already done in this area. We visited the Agricultural Greenhouse Gas Research Centre and were shown around by its director, Dr Harry Clark. This was wonderful for me as I realised yet again that when you focus on solutions you have a great opportunity to make progress. This was hard science, and it showed that animals fed on high-value pasture like ours emitted no more CO_2 than those fed on poor pasture – but, as we had already found, faster finishing hugely lowered emissions. It was very clear that increasing efficiency would be the only driver of success in finding environmental solutions.

Then in late September, farmer Zach Mounsey and I were Argentina-bound. It was a busy week of meeting scientists and academics, as well as travelling to experimental farms where we met a lot of wonderful farming folk. Once again I saw what happens when political process is locked down in division. City people were against country people, and country people were against city people. The country people have accumulated wealth and spend their entire time trying to preserve that, rather than being productive. In fact, as in Uruguay, they rarely visit their farms and live in comfort in the cities, and the underbelly of their society pays the very heavy price.

In Buenos Aires there are massive slums where the desperation is as bad as you've ever seen. Argentina's got the potential to feed 600 million more people, just by raising their systems closer to world standard. But their political situation is so bad that they don't spend any time on that space.

We went to a grain farm where there was a surplus of grain. To keep food prices down, export tariffs have been put on most farmed produce. This was intended to force farmers to sell their food crops cheap to city people. But the farmers resisted and merely loaded huge amounts of grain into polythene bags for storage. There were masses of these bags, full of grain, everywhere in the countryside. However, they'd been discovered by armadillos, which poked their noses in through the plastic, and the grain just flowed out into the armadillos, which were having a very happy life indeed.

Then all of a sudden it rained heavily and the torn bags sat in the puddles. The grain expanded and the bags were all blown open. So all over Argentina not only did the people miss out, but so did the farmers.

It's a gridlock situation; I've never seen anything so bad. There's no collective vision at all.

Science professionals there had little enthusiasm because they could see all this off-direction stuff going on. They, too, were like the flea in the bowl. The ceiling they risked bashing their heads against was the dysfunctional political system, and the lack of constructive relationships between city and country. New Zealand farmers operate in a very supportive environment by comparison, and our farming efficiency is on a different planet. The hospitality in South America is great and I would jump at any opportunity to go back there again, but it left me with this huge feeling of frustration. When you have a dislocation between governments and business people, it paralyses everybody. My huge learning from that trip was that the world is about relationships, relationships, relationships.

33

SHAKY GROUND

My newfound resilience was about to be tested to its extreme.

The first earthquake came in 2013, 6.6 magnitude, its epicentre just 2.5 kilometres from our house, and 150 metres from our farm boundary.

I was up in the paddock that day cleaning up after a wind storm. I'd just picked up a log with the claw of our John Deere tractor when suddenly the world went crazy. I thought I was having a stroke, until I saw what was happening to the animals. They were all thrown to the ground, the sheep rolling around helplessly, their legs waving in the air, like tennis balls on a trampoline. But as soon as the shaking stopped, they got to their feet and ran together – all in a huddle of togetherness, seeking the comfort and security of each other.

Humans are no different, and I got back to the house as quick as I could. Wendy and I stood on our lawn as the aftershocks roared through. We heard all our stuff breaking in the house – precious things;

the china sets from Wendy's grandmother and great-grandmother. There was nothing we could do to save any of it.

It was almost a decade since I'd thrown off my depression and found hope again. In that time we'd transformed the way we farm our land. The solutions and thinking processes we'd developed had made us resilient, not only as farmers but also as human beings. But with that first earthquake I saw the black dog again for the first time in a long while. He was eyeing up our smashed windows and burst water systems, sniffing at our fear and trauma, snarling at all the work we needed to do to get back to where we'd been. I could see him, and for a few days he came pretty close.

I was lucky that time. I got a phone call from a guy, a local farmer who had escaped the damage. 'Anything I can do to help?' he asked.

'Nah,' I told him. 'I'm okay.' I probably also added what all us stoic types say at a time like this: 'I'm lucky. There are plenty of people worse off than me.'

He turned up the next morning with a basket of muffins his wife had baked. 'You're probably not okay,' he said.

He was right, of course. No one's okay after an experience like that. My mind had been going at a thousand kilometres an hour ever since the quake, but I'd actually done very little. Most depressed people think they're busy but really they're doing nothing. I hadn't realised the state I was in. He helped me get back in gear – called the insurance company, got the windows covered over – and he helped me get started on some basic stuff, until I knew I could do it myself again.

Over the next months we recovered from the quake. Our water tanks had been thrown around as if they were as light as balloons, so we put on flexible fittings. We made sure we had the ability to bring in a generator to pump water. Our brick chimney had fallen in, so we replaced it with a flue. Wendy put special liners in the cupboard to

With that first earthquake I saw the black dog again for the first time in a long while.

stop things moving around, and strapped a lot of items to the wall. In other words, we made our physical surroundings as earthquake-proof and resilient as possible. We simply didn't replace a lot of our stuff. It was, we realised, just *stuff*.

I didn't succumb to the black dog; I chased him off the property. Everybody has days of feeling really low – *everybody* – but I've learned to see and understand the difference between stress and goddamn disgusting depression.

And then came the second earthquake.

The second earthquake woke me from a beautiful sleep at two minutes after midnight on 14 November 2016. I wasn't worried for the first few seconds, but the usual pattern of a shake – a judder that's over reasonably quickly – didn't happen. Instead, there was a roaring sound, as if a freight train was about to crash through our house, and instead of abating, the shaking got worse. Wendy was awake, too. Things began smashing in the house, and we could hear the house itself fighting against the tremendous force being unleashed. We were in darkness, and all around us was violence – jolting, jarring and heaving. It was the most terrifying thing I've ever experienced, and it went on and on. Surely you're finished now, I thought, but instead the intensity increased. *We are in hell.* The ground itself was rejecting us, throwing us off, and there was nothing certain in the whole world. We clung to each other, and there was nothing we could do. We thought, this is it.

And then, after nearly two minutes, it subsided and we knew we were alive, but that was all we knew.

Later that day we found it had been 7.8 magnitude – a truly awesome force, sixty times more powerful than the 2013 quake. State Highway 1 was blocked by massive slips, train tracks spilled over the road, the coastline between Cape Campbell and south of Kaikoura was raised by between one and three metres, and 100,000 slips exposed the land as if it had been mauled by the claws of an enormous monster. The land was smashed. Mushed. Over the next week there would be more than 4000 aftershocks, many of them violent and terrifying, and of course they continued for months, constant reminders that we are not in control.

But for now we were alive. I grabbed the headlamp I keep hanging over my bedpost; it's been there ever since the first earthquake. Wendy had disappeared into the bed but I threw the bedclothes back and urged her out. I was extremely nervous of tsunami, given we are only about eight metres above sea level. So we both got dressed and then worked our way through the debris of glass and broken furniture to the utter shambles of my office, where I searched for my truck keys. Where were they? Finally I thought to look in the truck and there they were.

We drove down the valley a hundred metres to our stock manager's house. Darcy and his partner Meg were standing in the drive, the power lines to the house dangling down onto the ground. 'Get in,' I yelled. I've never seen an invitation to get in a truck so speedily taken up. I backed out of their drive just as our tractor driver, Mike, came speeding up the road, turned into our farm and drove straight past heading for higher ground. I could see he had his two boys with him.

But we drove south up Grassmere Road and called in at our farm cottage where Paul, one of our stockmen, was sitting in his car. 'Follow us,' I yelled, and we drove to the next neighbour. Soon we had the whole valley driving up the road to the top of the hill at our Glen Erin property. We could see the twinkle of other families on other hills in the distance as they, too, huddled together. Aftershocks roared up the valley. The kids were terrified, but we joked and laughed for their sake. Some had brought sleeping bags and rugs and we chatted about events, while listening for news on the radio.

The phone systems were down, so after a while we decided to drive to Ward to see if our daughter Alice and family were okay. We drove over the farm track, and high up on the Kaka Ridges deer came out of one of our fenced-off native areas. They looked as scared as we were, just standing on the track in the headlights of the truck.

We could see the flashing lights of emergency services in Ward. Alice wasn't at home, but the tenants of our other house there, who were trying to sleep in their car, told me that everyone was safe (though the house was now uninhabitable), and that Alice had gone to help her husband Lochy's elderly parents.

While all this was happening, aftershocks continued to roar through. Wendy and I went back home for some sleep, but we had only just got into bed when a massive aftershock came through and we thought, this is not the place for us! So we rose again and drove to Blenheim to fill some drums with diesel, realising we were very low on supply and how crucial fuel would be for the next period.

The moon that night, the biggest moon I have ever seen, cast its pale light over our devastated landscape. I looked up at it, and it seemed to wink at me as if to say, *Take that, fella.*

34

BUILDING RELATIONSHIPS

Gratitude. It's a humble emotion, an unconditional state of mind. When I was in my bad space I was ungrateful for my life, but when I got better my gratitude came back. I became grateful for the people who were in my life, grateful for the return of the rain, grateful for absolutely everything – and my gratitude has remained. It is pure thankfulness for every bit of good fortune. And that was the incredible feeling that began to build inside me after the 14 November earthquake. My family was alive and everything else could be fixed. It could all have been so much worse.

This was a test of my own resilience. Needing to express my sense of gratitude, I turned my attention to the wider community, for which that earthquake had been devastating. We've had tragedies before – teenagers killed on the roads, fires, drought – but nothing in my lifetime affected the district as badly as 14 November. The damage was different from house to house, farm to farm and business to business. But everyone had experienced the fear. It was more than anyone had faced before, and when you go through that you realise most people travel the same course. Never before have I witnessed the population of an area being brought together so strongly. It's similar to what happens during a war – a dreadful experience, but one that's shared by everybody.

First, there's a massive burst of adrenaline and people get incredibly busy around individual and community survival. You lose track of the energy you burn through. The violent aftershocks make sleep massively difficult, and that further compounds and debilitates your emotional state.

Exhaustion seeps in. About fourteen days after that quake, a meeting was called at Ward Hall. I looked at the faces, hollow, spent, no life in them. People crying – people I wouldn't expect to see cry, ever. The vulnerability was chilling. If we got another shock, how would we cope?

My experience from the first earthquake showed me that there's always a process to work through. As a more resilient person, I've learned to manage the fear and anxiety better by identifying what I need to worry about, and what I can't do anything about.

Our own business had been back up and running within twelve days; our system had proved resilient, and the changes we'd made after the first quake had stood up well. But I could see that a large percentage of people in the community were totally tripped up. Looking at those distraught faces, I remembered how violating it is to have your home wrecked. It's not easy to cope with, perhaps particularly for women, and men don't cope if their wives are not happy. (I reckon women, however, cope well even if their men aren't happy – an interesting twist on male–female relationships. It's certainly been true of me and Wendy.)

I thought back to when my friend had come over to help me, and how welcome and necessary that had been. I saw that many people were as out of gear as I'd been. And I knew that often, when people were offered help, they turned it down. *We're fine,* they'd say. But no one was fine.

I got in touch with the Rotary Club, the Lions Club and a church group in Blenheim, and we gathered a group of about thirty people the following Saturday morning. We all brought our lawnmowers, and our own smoko, and we went round to all the places we knew where people were doing it hard and needing a hand.

'Today,' I told the volunteers, before we all headed out, 'you are going to be doing mundane tasks but you will never, ever mow lawns at the rate of reward and benefit that you will do today.'

Those people mowed lawns, cut hedges, cleaned windows. You might think those are unimportant tasks, but those small acts of mercy and assistance were hugely uplifting for the recipients.

Fear and anxiety are two of the most draining human emotions. After the earthquake, I talked to so many people teetering on the brink of serious depression – I was going around spilling out my one-liners. The one that got such a positive response was this: Fear has two meanings. Forget Everything And Run; or Face Everything And Rise. That meant so much to everyone who heard it; it's simple language, but it created a mind resource for people that encouraged them to actively respond to their challenges. Sometimes the simplest things have the most impact.

My family from Auckland rang and asked what they could do. A niece worked at Ecostore and they arranged a huge shipment. BNZ and Dominion Salt joined with Wendy and me in putting together care parcels of Ecostore products and grocery vouchers. We delivered 140 of these between Grassmere and Clarence. This gave me a chance to meet people and see how they were faring. I identified about seven people who needed more help and we arranged for support. I am still counselling some of them.

Those weeks following the 14 November earthquake were amazing for me. With Fraser in charge of the farm, I was able to shift my agenda towards being out and about in the community, helping where I could. Because I've publicly acknowledged my own struggle with depression, it frees people up to talk to me about what they're going through. People called me to talk; and as I went around, people would say, you'd better go and see so-and-so . . .

A 7.8 magnitude earthquake is an obvious physical trauma, and of course people and communities are shaken both literally and figuratively. But just as the earthquake causes hillsides to crumble, exposing the earth beneath the surface, so it strips away the topcoat people wear over their lives. Such trauma reveals the existing difficulties beneath. For many of these people the earthquake was the last straw. I could see there was real danger for people who had probably been accumulating emotional stuff for years, struggling but just keeping it together. People who had been living with trauma, or with an ill family member, or with health issues of their own, suddenly could not cope with the extra burden. Those who had been living for years with depression suddenly could not cope at all. I can relate to that. I believe I was walking wounded ever since the trauma of Wendy's cancer and everything else that happened back in 1993. I hadn't taken the opportunity to acknowledge the impact, or to grow myself, and so I had made myself vulnerable – already staggering when the drought delivered its knockout punch.

Some people who had run from earthquake-stricken Christchurch now found themselves at the mercy of the land again, without having resolved their initial issues. *Leave on your own terms* is my advice to anyone thinking of just running away.

In 1998 when it all seemed impossible, I would love to have got in my car and driven off. Anywhere. Nowhere. But I didn't know where

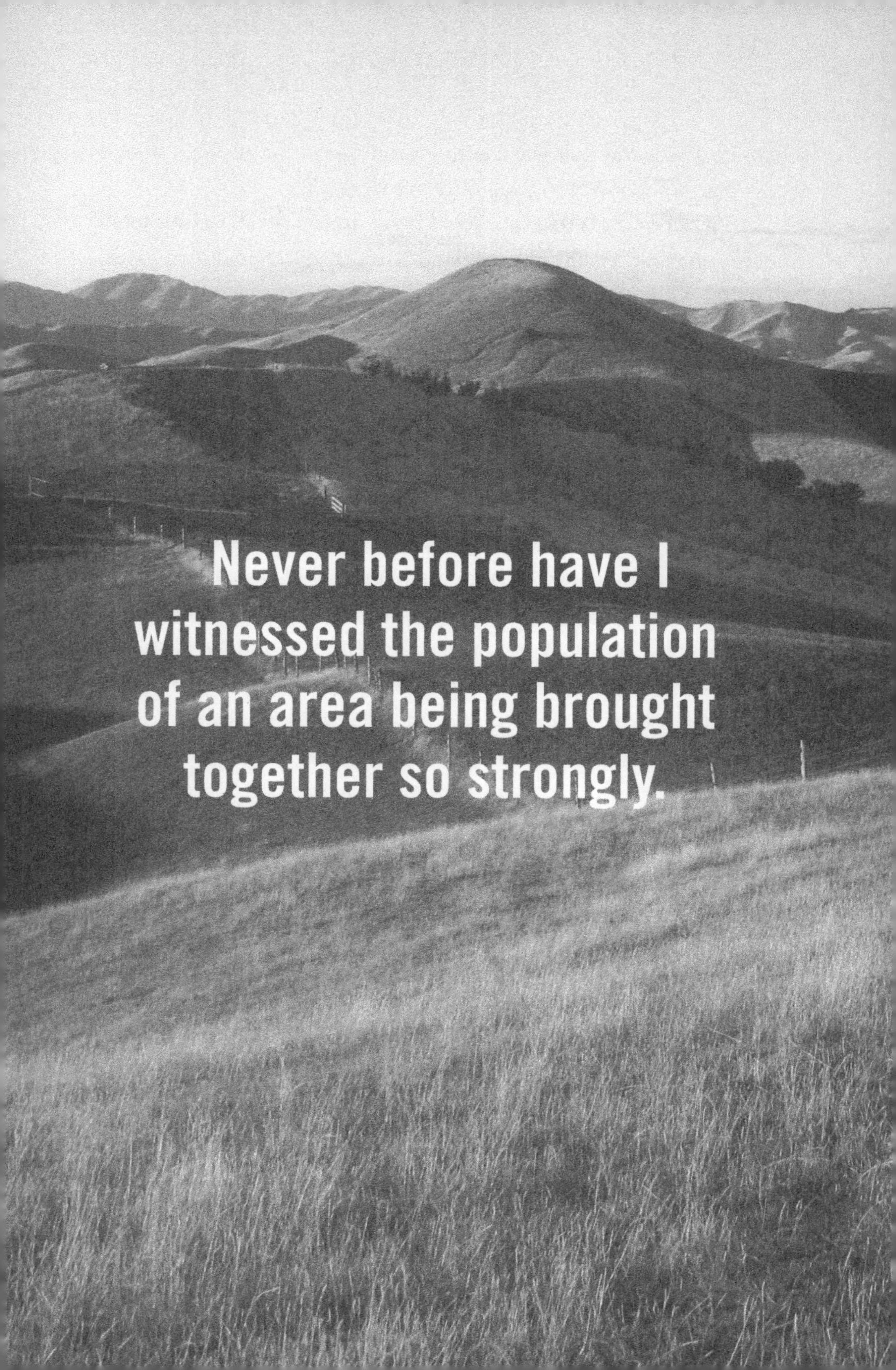

Never before have I witnessed the population of an area being brought together so strongly.

to go. I've learnt that you can never run from your troubles. Each of us has to find a way to bounce forward, not back.

I put it to them that now was a good time to get their lives totally back on track. Troubles signal that it's time to get the solution process rolling. When you think like this your troubles turn into opportunities, and that creates that great word *hope*, which we all need.

I helped one lady who was so traumatised she would not re-enter her house. Through my Facebook page I had advised that I was giving away 'free hugs', and people started to contact me with the names of those who needed them. This lady certainly seemed to need one. 'I'll give you a hug,' I said.

'Please don't,' she said. 'I smell too bad. It's days since I had a shower. I'm too scared to go in the house.' I still leaned forward and gave her a huge hug. Next day I came around with our lawnmower and cut her lawns. A few weeks later she was getting back some confidence. It's a slow and hard process, but one that delivers great personal reward.

Fatigue and stress mean people lose sight of what is healthy behaviour. Men in particular have been trained that they mustn't show emotion for fear of seeming weak, so it's very hard for them at times like this. I see anger and blame, but it's nearly always about much more personal issues than just the matter at hand.

I'm not a counsellor, but because I've walked in the same shoes as the people around me, they are able to open up. They know I won't judge; they know I'm like they are.

Nor am I a religious person, but I am a spiritual person in that I believe human beings have the ability to reach for a higher sense than just themselves. Yet many people today don't know where to reach, and have nothing bigger than themselves to believe in. The need that was served by the church has been replaced by going to the gym. That works up to a point, but if you don't have something deeper, you can be left feeling very empty when something bad happens. For me, it comes down to relationships, relationships, relationships. As a society we pay little attention to human relationships. No well-meaning government agency can take the place of social connectivity.

People say, it's a bugger of a crisis that doesn't achieve some good. My own experience shows me that we achieve little at our peaks; our valleys are our opportunities. Every time something bad happens, I know I will grow.

Before this year's out, something rough will happen to each and every one of us. Bound to. There will be something that is beyond our control, but it will happen and it will make life seem hard for a while. But I have the basic premise that we will bounce forward from our troubles. Once my initial feelings – of grief, irritation, fear, whatever it is – have settled, I will look for the thing that's worthwhile about what's happened. At Bonavaree we don't talk any more about bouncing *back*. Because if you analyse what's happened and you talk about bouncing *forward,* that starts a momentum that is hard to stop.

This is what I'm about. This is resilience. Resilience isn't about not having bad times; it's about having the tools to recover from difficulties, to adapt, to bounce forward. Part of resilience is being honest and self-aware about the feelings we carry inside ourselves. What's really going on? If we cover things over and lie to ourselves, as I did, then our whole foundation in life is shaky. Our most precious relationships begin to sink as if they are on soft ground. If an individual isn't resilient, they can't create resilient relationships.

We have to give human beings permission to open their hearts when they need to. We have some big problems in this country. Why, in New Zealand, are we twice as likely to die by our own hand as in a motor accident?

Like me, none of these people had ever sought help before, or talked to anyone. Yet they were living very close to the edge. Below the tragedy of suicide is a huge pyramid of depression, and when something like the 14 November earthquake happens, the top is ripped off and we see what lies below.

This is something we all have to work together to address. This is our social capital. It's as important as financial capital; it's as important as natural capital. This is at the heart of what I do now. My efforts are all about building social resilience so we can build our social capital. If any of those three legs is broken, the stool will fall over. And we see this, all over the country, in communities where there is social dysfunction, depression and suicide.

When bad things happen we have a choice: to cope with them or not to cope. Coping doesn't mean finding solutions straight away – it might just be asking for help or taking the first step. Where I've got to in the work I've been doing on my own top paddock is that the key to where you are now lies in where you're heading. Today is the day. You can't recreate yesterday. The earthquake – or whatever it is that's happened – has happened. What now?

We need to go through our stressed, broken phase. We need to acknowledge what's been lost, and how much that hurts. Then as we move out of that, we begin to accept there are things we can't change. But there's always a possible course of action, a choice about what comes next. I look for my circle of influence, and that helps me prioritise so I can move forward.

This goes beyond the personality you're born with. These are techniques, habits of mind, that we can all learn. I wasn't always like this. The old Doug used to carry the worries of the world, but today's Doug thinks, *Is this in my circle of influence?* Worry is the most wasteful emotion.

I've seen what our community went through, is still going through:

there's no one that was so strong they didn't need help. We're like the sheep: we cluster together for support when things are tough. We need to build resilient communities so we can be strong together when things go wrong.

35

THE RESILIENT FARMER

You can't dodge life. You have to deal with it.

I no longer look at life as easy, or assume that everything will be roses. I expect bad; I know it will come – but I know how to handle these times. From these times great things will come, provided I'm prepared to ride the storm and learn each time. Life has turned a once volatile man into a calm, happy man with huge capacity to cope and manage – a man who has a high degree of resilience.

I was driving in my truck one day, listening to the radio, when a woman began talking about rural suicides. She was from Federated Farmers and had been at a coroner's hearing into the death of a farmer whose quad bike had toppled over, killing him. On average five people die and 850 are injured in New Zealand each year while riding quad bikes. She made the point that many more people die by suicide than in quad-bike accidents. That year, 2013, there were seventy-eight rural suicides – a high number that includes not just farmers but people who live in rural areas. About 21 of those would have been directly farm-related. It seems strange to say it now, but I had no idea how bad things were. If suicide is the tip of the iceberg, it's a mighty big iceberg of depression and suffering hiding beneath the surface of our rural communities.

Every single one of those suicides is a tragic story: a person, a family, a community in pain.

That's wrong, I thought. *That's absolutely wrong.*

I arrived home in a daze. By that stage I'd been doing Beyond Reasonable Drought events – a lot of talking about lucerne and water utilisation and money and things like that. I never talked about my emotional problems in any depth. Really, I swept them under the table, as it was still very raw stuff and it was easier just to park it. But now . . . with a shock I realised that I'd been totally wasting my time.

As it happened, the reason I was in my truck that day was I'd been heading home to do a phone interview with Jamie Mackay on his radio show, *The Country*. It's a regular slot, and I always have a bit of choice around what we talk about. That day, when Jamie asked what I had on, I just blurted it out. 'The real issue I want to talk about with you today is suicide. Back fifteen years ago, I was the guy suffering from depression.'

Jamie contacted me a couple of days later. 'We have never, ever had such a response to anything we've ever done,' he told me.

I had touched a nerve. Emails, phone calls. People asking me to help, or to talk. The Mental Health Foundation asked me to do a video. And that's how it started – that was really the birth of The Resilient Farmer.

For a long time I had talked about sustainability. How could I make my life and my farm sustainable? But now I realised that wasn't enough. In order to farm or do anything sustainably, we need to build our resilience. People say country people are resilient, but I suddenly saw that wasn't as true as we like to think. The high rural suicide rate, and our knowledge that suicide is the tip of the iceberg, means something really wrong is going on.

Beyond Reasonable Drought lost its appeal. We were looking, I realised, at change way beyond just wet or dry.

I couldn't figure out how to do it. But then, as often happens, life took me in the right direction. A photographer came to Bonavaree to take photos of me for the FMG website. He suggested I come to Wellington to meet a friend of his, Cam McDuff, director of design company Wonderlab. I did exactly that, and Cam in turn introduced me to the idea of brand development. I didn't know anything about that, and didn't realise I'd even established a brand. He helped me clarify my brand. The Resilient Farmer: we arrived at that together and it was perfect. He mapped a direction forward. He showed me that while I had relationships with a lot of businesses in the agribusiness sector, I had no decent structure, so no way currently for them to support me.

With his design, The Resilient Farmer took shape. We created a three-tier structure for sponsors: one Platinum partnership at a cost of $50,000, four Gold partnerships at $30,000 each, and then a third tier of advertising partnerships. We put together a striking and comprehensive 'partnership proposal' booklet so I could approach the kind of sponsors I wanted. My aim was to create a commercial model – to commercialise the process of making people think better. I have massive confidence in the power you create once you develop value. It incentivises people.

I wanted The Resilient Farmer to bring together high-performing companies who understand the ups and downs of farming; to unite those companies with farmers; and to introduce them to new tools both in the office and on the farm so they grow wealth – both financially and in their inner selves.

Cam emailed me the finished design and told me the hard copy was in the mail. But I couldn't wait. I can never wait. I was so excited, I emailed it straight to the companies I wanted to sponsor me. BNZ, Allflex, Beef + Lamb New Zealand, FMG Advice and Insurance, Seed Force.

'We're offering you the chance to go on a positive journey of change with the New Zealand farming industry . . .' I told them.

Would the companies see it the same way I did?

I sat there in a big hole, waiting. Worrying. *This ain't going to work.* I needed at least two or three in order to have the confidence to go ahead.

Then, forty-eight hours later, BNZ rang. 'We're only interested in one level of sponsorship,' they said. 'We want Platinum and if we can have that, we're in.'

Over the next couple of days, everyone else came in as Gold, and I was funded. I soon picked up three advertising partners as well – Dominion Salt, Farmax and Coach Approach. All good to go. I shot out and bought branded goodie bags and printed information sheets.

Planning my speaking tour, I'd ring a few people in each area to find the best local accountancy practice. Accountants already have a relationship with the best farmers in the district, and it was those farmers I wanted to talk to and influence. The top will pull up the rest.

Then I'd ring the accountancy firm. Would they be interested in hosting an event? And they never once said, 'How much will it cost?' They said, 'Oh my God, thank you for ringing us.'

My original plan was for thirty-one events nationwide.

We kicked off in Balclutha in February 2015. I arrived at the venue and nervously asked the host, 'How many?'

'Two hundred,' he said. 'That's all we can take. She's full.'

'We're away!'

And by the end of that year I'd rolled my sleeves up at sixty-six presentations and was completely spent.

'You've taken on too much,' Derrick Moot told me when he saw my schedule.

'Get away!' I responded, 'It's only an hour and a half on my feet and an hour of questions . . .'

But planned time off fell to bits as I crammed more and more in, and exhaustion started to creep in. Then came the week when I flew to Australia for some work, came home late at night, rose early to catch up on book work for the farm and by 8 a.m. was on my way into Blenheim to pick up some material I needed for my Wanaka event that night. That was when I really reached the limit of my capabilities.

It was much tougher than I'd expected. I relied wholly on Wendy to keep me safe; I'd said at the outset that I needed to have her with me, as I couldn't have done all that travelling on my own. I'd done it for the Beyond Reasonable Drought tour, but I hated it. I'd walk into these rooms all pumped up and there would usually be around 150 people. I absolutely love getting an audience and working them; those are the times when all the lights come on for me.

Afterwards, though, when I go back to my motel and – *bang* – it's gone, everyone's out of my life, there's nothing doing, I'm exhausted, but the brain's still going at a thousand miles an hour. I don't have an off switch in public settings, so Wendy rescued me, determinedly pulling me away when it was time to go.

It's a dangerous thing to wear your heart on your sleeve, but mine doesn't know where else to live so it has to stay there and I have to cope with whatever comes. Often, after my talks, somebody will approach me wanting to talk about stuff that's going on for them. I don't think people should dabble in this area if they really don't have any sensitivity towards it, but I believe there's a space in there for people who have got time to listen. Sometimes that's all I do – and most people actually don't need much more than a few minutes of listening. Sometimes I follow up with Skype or an email or a phone call. Sometimes I'll put them on to somebody else – I know quite a few people around the place now, counsellors and psychologists, but I always check up to make sure the person I put them in touch with was helpful for them.

I've learned so much from the people who come up to talk, and it's really helpful to compare the journeys. A lot of people can't – or think they can't – talk to the people around them because they're not sure how they'll take it, but people feel very comfortable talking to me because I've made a declaration. I've been where they are; I've walked in their shoes. I'm a very open person and I think people respond to that and can open up to me in return.

I make no claims to be a psychologist, and I don't promise to help or make things better. I just tell them the truth: I'm a guy that's been through this and I've come out the other side. I can try to help you if you want, by sharing my story and what I've learnt. If they accept that invitation they've accepted it with a risk profile attached.

But the big thing with the work I do is this: I don't want to be sitting with someone who's broken like I was. Wouldn't it be good if people didn't get to that stage? I want to be empowering somebody who hasn't broken. The hard part is, a lot of people don't recognise the need for that kind of learning until they have broken.

36

RESILIENCE PIPELINE

Connect.
Give.
Take notice.
Don't personalise problems that are not yours.
Keep learning.
Be active.

These six things keep me happy.

Connect. I understand wanting to isolate yourself. It feels like a safe place. If you isolate yourself, no one can touch you, no one can challenge you or threaten you. You are cocooning yourself inside the familiarity and 'comfort' of your own thoughts. But it's an illusion. It's 100 per cent in the wrong direction. The only place such isolation can lead is to a smaller and more fearful life.

If you only ever communicate with people who think the same

way you do, you won't create a fertile ground for yourself to grow. But when you change the way you look at things – let go of your tree trunk – you open the possibility for change and growth.

Give. We've turned into a less giving society. We think we're too busy and stressed to give to others. People who are depressed almost invariably have stopped giving altogether. I was brought up in a giving home, but when I got into my bad place I didn't want to give anyone anything. I thought I was doing so badly, I was angry at the very idea of giving anything away. But giving is one of the most emotionally rewarding things that you can ever do. It's ironic: we think it's about giving to others, but when we give we end up rewarding ourselves so richly. So: do more, give more, give 120 per cent. Giving is one of the best insurance policies.

Take notice. Take notice of what's happening in the world; the world's always changing and you are a part of the social fabric. You think you want to opt out of the world, but the world won't opt out of you. Depressed people are in lockdown – they don't want to take notice of anything else but their own troubles. Yet we all exist in this world, so we need to know what's going on.

I've seen this happen to rural people – they are in a cocoon. They might own a little block of land and think, I'm going to grow a few cabbages and cucumbers and I'll sell them at the end of the road and get $50 a week and that'll buy all the inputs I need. But everyone else around there has put in grapes and they're getting a million dollars out of their place and suddenly your rates bill is $20,000 – but you hadn't noticed that process happening.

Don't personalise problems that are not yours. Let go of the bits that aren't yours. Envy, anger and blame are all so draining because you're constantly thinking about what other people have done rather than empowering yourself to get to a better place.

As a society we don't deal well with conflict or differences of opinion. How many of us have defriended someone on Facebook just because they said something we didn't like? We turn our backs, rather than have a conversation. It's because we're afraid of anger – but pretending differences don't exist doesn't solve the problem.

As soon as I feel angry now, I get worried. If somebody does something to cause me anger I just immediately think, no, I've got to deal with this. I have to deal with it, then move on. This is a huge part of my emotional management.

Keep learning. For me, this is behind every success, every joy that I now have in my life. My life has become a constant journey of learning. Learning new things blasted me out of the stagnation of my forties and continues to provide me with riches – and I don't just mean material wealth – beyond my wildest dreams.

Be active. This is a vital part of how I keep well in both mind and body. Back in the late 1990s, when I was in some of my worst days, I saw a little ad in the newspaper. *Try squash,* it said. And I thought, I will. So I went along to the open day and I ran around that court and got soaked in sweat and physically exhausted, and I loved it. It made me feel mentally stronger. I ended up as president of the squash club. As well as reintroducing me to physical fitness, it introduced me to a whole group of people who didn't have a drought. 'What a cracker of a day,' they'd say, and I learned to accept that it probably was.

I also managed to keep up sailing, although by that stage I didn't have a boat of my own and was crewing for others. So I had one sport that was all about accuracy of angles and maths and physics, and another that was all about harnessing the energy of nature so as to turn it in a constructive direction, and they matched perfectly for my character.

More recently, I bought a bike and I ride every day, often with Wendy.

Human beings are not made to sit all day at our computers. We are physical beasts, made to catch food, dig the garden, chase our prey. Our bodies are not made for this lifestyle we've created of softness and ease.

Those six things are my positive answer – my recipe for a happy life. But there's something else that lies underneath them all, like a foundation stone, without which all those six things will never get a strong foothold. And that is to get help.

Get help. Accept that you possibly have a problem. Read the stuff on *www.depression.org.nz*, or *www.farmstrong.co.nz.* Other people can't wait to help you. Seeking help is the bottom line. And one more word of advice: if you get into a bad place, *now* is a great word. Do something now. Just a tiny wee task, it doesn't matter how small.

Until we've been broken, we don't know what it feels like. And then we find out, and we forget how to return to our happy place. The only way we can rediscover that happy place is in tiny steps – five minutes of something . . . then ten minutes.

You won't set out towards resilience on Monday and be resilient by Friday. But when you've taken some tiny steps, they become building blocks towards hope. Achievement builds hope, and that's your pathway out of depression. Don't be afraid to take small steps. My own dream was to ride my bike to the finish line, without stopping; my reality was more about getting past the starting line.

As Johnny Peter said to me one day: 'If you're not going to learn to slow down and take small wins you'll blow yourself apart with frustration.'

As a guest of Consolidated Pastoral Company, one of Australia's largest privately owned agrifood businesses, I was taken to visit an auto assembly plant in Brisbane. There, Mack and Volvo trucks are assembled and, of course, I was expecting to see a lot of robots at work. But there was only one, busily doing the relatively humble task of putting windscreens into frames. All the rest of the work was manual. As I came to understand the process I was watching, I became absolutely inspired.

Every truck was assembled to order, each slightly different from the last, according to the requirements of the customer.

A man went out with a forklift and he picked up, out of heaps of chassis, the correct bit of chassis for that truck, and from there the thing was pressed, bolted, painted, the engine and wheels assembled – all according to individual requirement.

And every thirty-eight minutes, a new truck emerged from the factory.

There were sixty of us in the visiting party that day. Fifty-nine were looking at them as trucks – but not me. I was looking at them as if they were people. This, I thought, is a model we can use.

Into my mind came the wonderful possibility of a Resilience

Pipeline of work-ready, life-ready people. We start with a person, we assess what knowledge and skills they have and what journey and destination they want. Then we ask: what do we need to add to this person to have them coming out the other end of this assembly line, future-ready? The capability we will bolt on to each person is individualised to the journey that person wants to live.

In my view, our education system tends to prepare people en masse, but in reality nearly everyone has an individual task and an individual destination. So, just like the trucks, we need to start personalising education to make people more purpose-ready for the life they want to live. This is the direction I want to take.

37

THE POOL OF CHANGE

I have become a resilient farmer.

As debate intensifies over the future of farming, I salute those in the industry who face the future with resilience, who bounce forward from the challenges.

Few other occupations align as closely with life and nature. We live every day so close to nature, so terrified by its power – in drought, flood, fire and hurricane – and so humbled by its beauty. We work first-hand with this power and know that any day, any hour, our work can be totally broken or enhanced, and we learn just to get up again and keep going. In my turn at the tiller of Bonavaree I have been smashed down and broken, I have been lifted up and praised – these are the valleys and peaks of a farming life.

Farmers get right up close and personal with the basic elements of life and the natural world and give them a bit of help. We produce huge volumes of quality food for our consumers and know that they

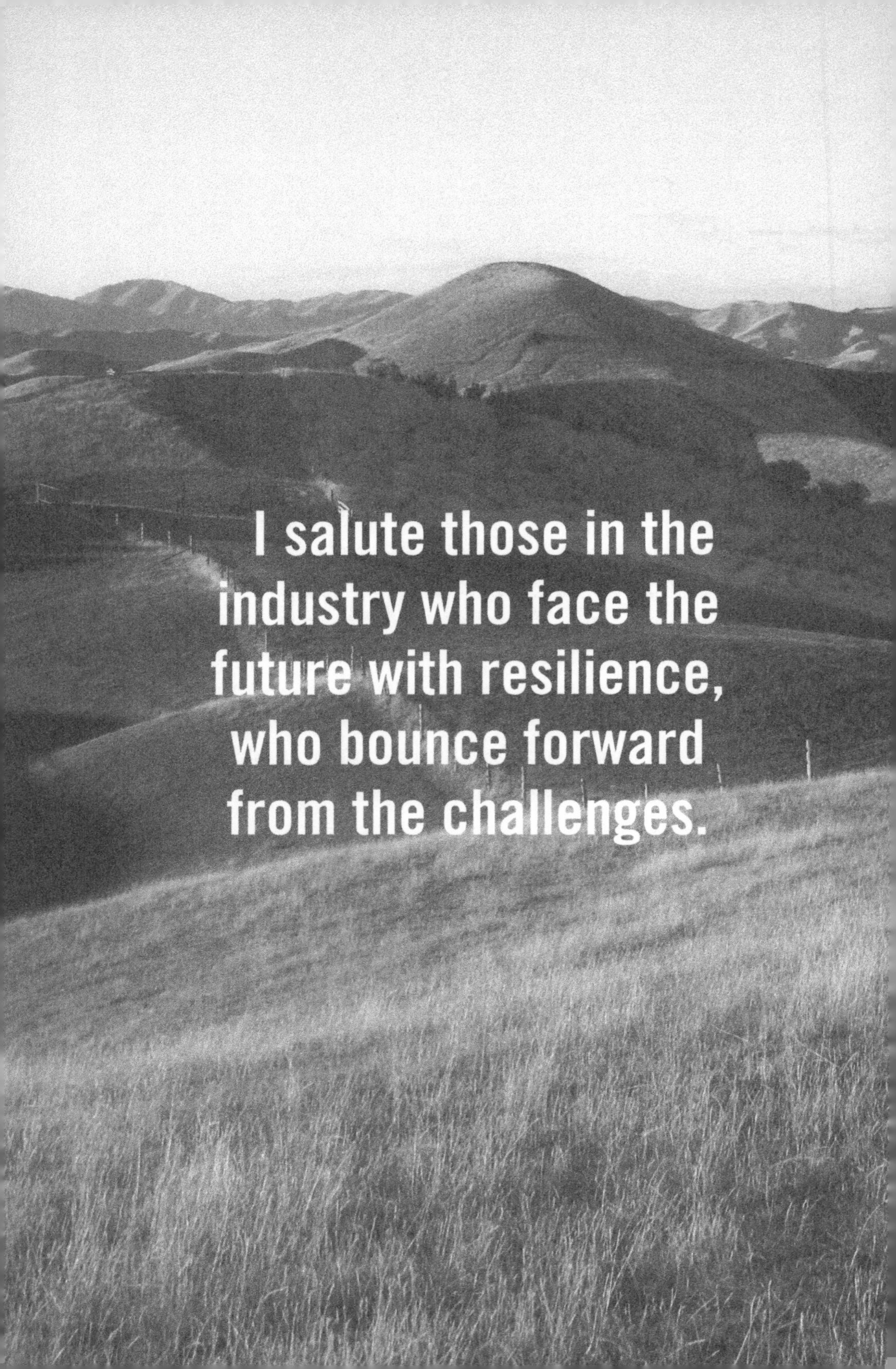

I salute those in the industry who face the future with resilience, who bounce forward from the challenges.

hold our product in the highest regard.

At Bonavaree we know that today, by the hour, we are making our land better for future generations. We have made such advances. I remember when our sheep needed our help to lamb, yet over time we developed the breed so they can do it all wonderfully by themselves, mostly producing twins. And I remember systems where water was only half as useful as it is today.

Today I look at Bonavaree with a huge sense of pride. On a daily basis I am but an observer now, just paying the bills and giving distant support, watching a wonderful team under Fraser implement leading-edge processes, day after day.

When social researcher Amanda Lynn came to Marlborough to research our crop of local entrepreneurs, she helped me gain such insight into myself. Working with Amanda taught me that I needed to feel value in my work, and when I cast my mind back over my time in farming my value cup overflows. Winning the South Island Farmer of the Year – for me the Rugby World Cup of farming – and the Landcorp Agricultural Communicator of the Year are among my greatest times. Communication is the only way to help others grow their ability, and that's what I want to do now: turn people to face the future, not just pat themselves on the back about the past.

If you believe, as I do, that everything created will fail if it is not attended to, then you will also agree with me that *the future creates the present*. When you can see where you want to be in the future you will make the best daily decisions to get to that place. So in my mind there is no place called the finish, no place called 'made it', because as soon as you are there, it's time to start the next job, to check some other part of the system, the work, the challenge.

My farm weaning is almost complete. Wendy and I will move

off the farm in the not-too-distant future, for the greater well-being of the farm; younger heads need their time. Moving to a new adventure will be emotionally easy for us both, but what's hard is the mechanics. Farms have massive capital value and low return on that capital. We've been doing a lot of consultation over the succession process. We employed a specialist facilitator and had a day at home with everybody where we all talked and cried – left nothing in the cupboard. Moving our life's work to other family members seems as vital as life itself, and it's a full-frontal 'why' for me. Why did I bother, why did I get out of bed, why did I cry, why did I laugh?

As I write, I can hear our grandchildren running into the house, the fifth generation of Averys to grow with the freedom that Bonavaree allows. I can hear them talking to Wendy: 'Nana, have you got biscuits in the tin?' We love watching them on the farm, seeing our core values being implanted on those replacement stock.

Tomorrow's Bonavaree will be different. Over the last few years the farm has made a step change in its process. After we won South Island Farmer of the Year, I asked one of the judges, Barry Brook, former chief executive of PGG Wrightson and also of Synlait Farms, if he would become my mentor. He agreed.

'I'll be a difficult bastard,' I said.

'I know, I can already see that.'

One of the first things he said was, 'Why don't you set up a board?'

'What good would that do?' I asked.

'You're getting pretty big. If you want to go bigger you'll just end up in trouble if you don't.'

So we did. I was chairman for a while, and then recently I stood aside and Barry became chairman of Bonavaree. Why would I do that? Because I suddenly realised we had all that horsepower; why would I want to stand in the way of somebody who was clearly better at that job? What this farm needed in the governance area was the strongest leadership we could get, and I wasn't that person.

That was just the start of a whole new way of agriculture.

In the future Bonavaree will probably have a different financial structure, one that invites others to be a part of its growth. Those partners will not only need to share the family's vision and values, they will also need to have value to add themselves. The complexities of future agriculture will require participants with far greater skills than one family can muster on its own. So I predict a new ownership structure and this will enable greater growth and wider contribution. It's reversing the trends of thirty years, where many have been pushed away from agriculture, to invite others to return to this exciting world of food production and land management. Along with that, the work and jobs offered at Bonavaree as time goes on will be highly desirable to progressive-minded people. Black singlets will be just a part of our folklore.

I can see the introduction of exciting technologies that will transform both productive capability and consumer relationships, and I can see overlay business developing, where the land platform becomes a park for human activities like walking, biking and education – maybe even allowing others to build their own parks on our land protected by covenant.

Technology will continue to take us into a healthier future for our land. We will soon be able to do amazing things, such as trace all our fertiliser, easily measure food density and quality, predict all outcomes from genetic development, and grow plants that will make what we use today look poor.

Climate change will continue to be a challenge but also an opportunity. Crops and animals we had never thought about having at Bonavaree will progressively appear, and new income channels will be developed.

We are on the first step of a new stairway. The climb will be hard, and no one can see the top, but at least we are climbing. We are guided forward by our core thinking about relationships – relationships with land, systems, people and, perhaps most important of all, ourselves.

I take a look in the mirror. That's where I have to start.

That's the change factor. When I started with myself and my own thought patterns, I travelled in the opposite direction from blame and excuse. I recognised the power I have to create my own behaviour to create a better life. Once I understood that, my life changed, and it's never stopped changing since.

Behind every sunset is a sunrise.

Dad was my greatest mentor. Even on his deathbed, preparing to leave this world, he wanted to add value to me. 'Doug,' he said, as I held his hand, 'greed is the greatest sin.'

I have pondered that ever since. Was he warning me off buying more land? Was he telling me to stop the growth that was starting to appear at Bonavaree? No. I believe he was telling me to *give*. Give back to the world I live in. Give people the confidence to grow their own minds. Give every day my best shot. Share the knowledge that grows from my endeavours, to those who wish to watch or listen. Become a teacher in giving and empowerment. Have the courage to go out there and release my learning.

I feel a huge sense of value for my hours, my days and my years. My journey has taken me to this wonderful space now where I'm a very free spirit. Who knows how long that will last, but it's good. It's so good.

A stone was dropped into the pool of change. The ripples are still moving. They are touching people's lives and inspiring them in their journey of discovery.

ACKNOWLEDGEMENTS

One day, in the depths of my despair, one man gave me hope. Derrick Moot inspired me to give life one more jump, one more huge effort to get out of my dark hole. Huge thanks for that, Derrick, and for your continued support to this day. I hope this book helps others to find the power, to look for hope.

Thanks also to John Ladley, who had the courage to demand I at least try one more time, and to all the people who worked in the Starborough Flaxbourne project, Don Ross, Barbara Stuart, Heather Collins, Kev Loe, Geoff Wiffen, Mike Watson, Marty Pattie, Rob Peter, Graeme Ogle, Paul Millen, Richard Hunter, Barrie Wills, Katie Nimmo, Gavin Kenny, and Alan Porteous from NIWA.

A special thanks to John Peter, the man with the courage and mana to inspire change. I loved every hour I spent with you, John . . . RIP. A mentor of extraordinary value.

Huge thanks to the amazing Margie Thomson, who captured my story in words, and to all the team at Penguin Random House New Zealand. Working with you has enriched my life.

To other people who inspired me along the way, all adding linking threads to my thinking: Parliamentary Commissioner to the Environment Dr Morgan Williams, Sir Paul Callaghan, Dr Amanda Lynn, psychologist Dennis Hoiberg and, more recently, Tim Minchin and futurist Thomas Frey.

Sir John Kirwan, who gave me the inspiration to share my broken story and who has given people permission to talk about the hardest subject, their emotional heart. He is the finest 'sir' in this country.

The companies that believe in my work and support us in The Resilient Farmer: BNZ, FMG, Allflex, Beef + Lamb, Lawson's

Dry Hills, Seed Force, Farmax, Dominion Salt, FarmIQ, MPI and Coach Approach.

And one of the world's best, my enabler, Shane McManaway, who opened my mind to a whole new world and introduced me to so many people who have in turn lifted me to face the winds of life.

Your attitude determines your altitude.

The staff, agents and business associates of Bonavaree who give our business amazing support, and Board Chairman Barry Brook, who has patiently guided us along the road.

My friends Charlie de Fegely, Scott Wishart and Matt Hood. You all add huge value to my days.

My extended family, who have always positively honked me to keep flying; in particular my father Graham, mother Joyce, brother Bas, sister Alison and the late Eric. And Fraser and Shelley, Ally and Lochy, Richie and Stacey, grandchildren Oliver, Quinn, Georgia and Eddie.

Most of all, my love and thanks to Wendy, who has hung on in there through one hell of a journey, who really became the last one, and had the courage to support me back into the world.

Life is love. You miss love, you miss life.

I cannot remove the holes in my wall but I live every day with gratitude to all who gave me a second chance in this wonderful thing called life.

When you change the way you look at things, the things you look at change.

Doug Avery

RESOURCES

Websites

The resources below are great starting points. Almost all have fact sheets, videos of people talking about their experiences, and sections that offer access to online and local resources. They contain information about managing mental health when things are tough, and most also have information about wellness and fostering resilience.

blackdoginstitute.org.au

Research institute with good resources on depression and mental health. (Australia)

depression.org.nz/get-better/self-help and **myjournal.depression.org.nz**

Information on depression and wellness for older adolescents and adults. Includes an online self-help programme (The Journal), with a focus on strategies and techniques to promote wellness and help you get through mild to moderate depression.

farmstrong.co.nz

Offers practical advice, tools and resources to help farmers understand such matters as nutrition, fatigue, exercise, emotional alarms and coping with pressure. Farmstrong also helps farmers connect with each other via its social media channels, through regional farmer ambassadors and at local events and workshops.

healthyfamilies.beyondblue.org.au

Comprehensive information on depression and anxiety, including warning signs and options for seeking help, helping others and getting well. (Australia)

mentalhealth.org.nz
The Mental Health Foundation website with an A to Z of resources, links to support services, a list of e-therapy options and resources, and a section on strategies to improve your wellbeing.

rethink.org
Mental health site with a comprehensive section for siblings of people with mental health and for carers of people with mental health concerns. (UK)

skylight.org.nz
Wide range of resources on grief, mental health and wellbeing for children, adolescents and adults. Includes information sheets, links to resources, resource packs, and individual and group counselling support in some areas.

smilingmind.com.au
Website and free app that facilitates use of mindfulness meditation to improve wellbeing. (Australia)

Phone, Text and Email

Alcohol Drug Helpline: 0800 787797
Depression Helpline: 0800 111757
Lifeline Aotearoa: 0800 543354
Suicide Crisis Helpline: 0508 TAUTOKO (0508 828865)
the lowdown: free text 5626, email team@thelowdown.co.nz

ABOUT THE CO-AUTHOR

Margie Thomson has had a long career working in magazines and newspapers, including as a feature writer and books editor for the *New Zealand Herald*, and feature writer and book reviewer for *Your Weekend*.

She has co-written many books, including John Kirwan's *All Blacks Don't Cry* and *Stand By Me* (co-authored with Dr Elliot Bell and Kirsty Louden-Bell), Ray Columbus' *The Modfather*, Malcolm Rands' *Ecoman*, three titles with Kelvin Cruickshank, Dr Lance O'Sullivan's *The Good Doctor*, and – with Angela McCarthy – *The Hungry Heart: Anorexia and Bulimia*. She has a Masters in Creative Writing, and she won the inaugural James Wallace Publication Prize in 2013.

Margie is married to James and has three children. She lives in Auckland.

A prominent and revered figure at the dawn of the professional age of rugby, John Kirwan seemed to live a charmed life.

But nobody knew that behind closed doors he was living a life of torment. Afflicted with depression for many years – including those as a high-profile sportsman – Kirwan was able to survive by reaching out, seeking help from those closest to him.

All Blacks Don't Cry is John Kirwan's story of hope, of working through the pain and living a full life. It is a poignant, inspirational and helpful example for anybody battling depression.

'May be the most useful book ever written by a New Zealand rugby player.'
—Philip Matthews, *Weekend Press*

Also available as an ebook

PENGUIN

UK | USA | Canada | Ireland | Australia
India | New Zealand | South Africa | China

Penguin is an imprint of the Penguin Random House group of companies,
whose addresses can be found at global.penguinrandomhouse.com.

First published by Penguin Random House New Zealand, 2017

10 9 8 7 6 5 4 3 2 1

Cover design by Kate Barraclough © Penguin Random House New Zealand
Text design by Emma Jakicevich © Penguin Random House New Zealand
Cover photograph by Rob Suisted, www.naturespic.com
All other photographs © Doug Avery
Printed and bound in Australia by Griffin Press, an Accredited ISO AS/
NZS 14001 Environmental Management Systems Printer

A catalogue record for this book is available from the National Library of New Zealand.

ISBN 978-0-14-377078-7
eISBN 978-0-14-377079-4

penguin.co.nz